SCIENCE
and the
NATION
Policy and Politics

J. Stefan Dupré and Sanford A. Lakoff

21068

Prentice-Hall, Inc. *Englewood Cliffs, N. J.*

1962

Foreword

In at least three American universities new seminars dealing with science and public policy have been started in the last several years. Recently I had the stimulating experience of conducting a graduate seminar devoted to this subject at M. I. T., and I have also met with seminar groups in two other institutions. I am convinced that the new mixture of science and political science is one of importance, that there is a wealth of interesting material to be examined and codified, and that we need to continue studying both the impact of science on government and foreign affairs, and the innovation in organization and policy this impact has caused. For these reasons I welcome this book as a needed contribution to the slight but growing body of literature devoted to science and government.

In expressing my gratification in the publication of this book, I would add three observations, hardly more than footnotes, bearing upon the interactions of technology and political science.

The first has to do with competence groups in government. In 1957 I had the privilege of accepting appointment as the first science adviser to the President of the United States. At the same time an independent science advisory committee, reporting directly to the President, was established. The format of these arrangements as made by President Eisenhower was such that they anticipated ways to reduce the dangers discussed by C. P. Snow in his Godkin Lectures on "Science and Government"—the dangers of biased or mistaken scientific advice which might cause political leaders to make bad decisions when dealing under conditions of secrecy with technical matters. From its beginning, the President's Science Advisory Committee was made independent of the Special Assistant to the President. It has always been able to report directly to the President if it disagrees with the Special Assistant. The committee can select its own chairman. So far it has selected the Special Assistant to fill this post, but it has done so on its own. In fact, when the committee was first established, some of the President's advisers, both political and scientific, urged that the Special Assistant be made ineligible to serve as its chairman in order to avoid any possibility of hindering independent decisions.

So far, however, the committee and the Special Assistant have worked well together, and the committee has brought to the Special Assistant—and to the President—a range of views, an objectivity, and an uninhibited freedom of comment that no single science adviser could hope to match.

In addition, the panel system of the "PSAC" has enabled the policy-making agencies of government to have roots deep in the creative non-government community of science.

All of this, I suggest, was an important innovation and advance in the use of competence groups by government, an invention jointly made by scientists and political scientists, and effectively used and relied upon by two Presidents. The chief defect is that there are no provisions made for contact with Congress. Quite understandably, Congress is now considering ways to provide a statutory underpinning for this mechanism (it was established by Executive Order), or to set up some new system. The danger is that in seeking to meet these problems, Congress will diminish the effectiveness of the present arrangement. I hope that a solution will be found which will provide the undeniably needed relationship with Congress and, at the same time, will enable first-rate, civilian, part-time advisers to be utilized.

My second observation is directed at the need for more scientists and engineers who are willing and qualified to accept responsibilities in public life. We do not now have enough competent scientists and engineers to fill the many important posts in government, particularly at the policy level, requiring both scientific and engineering competence, and the political sagacity and skills to survive in the arena of politics. Scientists and engineers are beginning to appear in state legislatures and in other elective offices, but there should be some in Congress as well. A technological society requires an adequate complement of scientists and engineers in the public arena if it is to deal wisely with all the great policy matters arising out of science and technology.

Herein lies the importance of the new programs in our universities and institutes of technology which bring together scientists and engineers with political scientists and students of public administration to study the ways their domains have interpenetrated each other.

My third observation is that the interface between science and political science is an area worthy of careful attention by both scientists and political scientists. It is here that the most effective bridges between science and the social sciences can be built. The study of science and government, as this book demonstrates, is revealing new and invigorating winds blowing in political science and public administration. It has been remarked that disciplines other than science and engineering may well begin to develop a dynamic quality, a rapidity of change, not unlike science. Political science may be such a field. It has also been frequently remarked that the United States has not produced a great political philosopher, certainly not since the Founding Fathers. Perhaps the interplay between science and politics may provide a new stimulus, as it did in a different way to Locke and Hobbes, for a new creative surge in this field.

These observations are by way of indicating reasons why I think this to be an important and timely book. While I would have interpreted or treated some of the topics differently from the authors, I nevertheless found the text exceedingly useful and stimulating and altogether a most valuable contribution to an unfolding area of scholarship.

J. R. KILLIAN, JR.

PREFACE

At no time has the United States been so dependent on science as it is now. Government promotion of scientific research has had a profound impact on industry and education, and demands an increasingly large share of federal spending. Scientists have acquired a new and unprecedented influence in the making of those "cardinal decisions" which, in C. P. Snow's plain but incisive words, "determine in the crudest sense whether we live or die."

This book has its origin in a new course introduced jointly by the authors for the Department of Government at Harvard in the Spring of 1960. The course, called "Science, Technology, and Politics," deals with a wide range of issues, including the impact of science upon social thought and the role of technology in industrial societies. In addition to these broader problems the course takes a close look at the formulation of science policy in the United States and the activity of scientists in politics. It is to these two practical questions that this book is devoted.

No single work of this size could possibly encompass as much detail and as many examples as an interested reader might wish. This book attempts to provide a concise survey of developments that are otherwise described only in a large number of government documents and secondary sources, many of them all but unavailable to the general reader. These developments are of such importance and such interest that we have felt ourselves more than justified in presenting this overall introduction and interpretation.

Readers who wish to pursue the subject further might begin most profitably with a number of works to which we ourselves are indebted. Among these is Don K. Price's *Government and Science,* the pathbreaking study of the relation of science to public policy. *The Bulletin of the Atomic Scientists,* ably edited by Eugene Rabinowitch, is an indispensable source of information and comment. The writings of A. Hunter Dupree, Robert Jungk, Charles V. Kidd, Ralph Lapp, and Dael Wolfle are most valuable.

The Science and Public Policy Program of the Harvard Graduate School of Public Administration has contributed greatly to the creation of this book through its library and secretarial facilities, and through the opportunities it has provided for discussion with eminent scientists and admistrators. Among our colleagues, Don K. Price and W. Eric Gustafson have been especially helpful, both in their careful criticism of the manuscript and as sources of advice and encouragement. Merle Fainsod guided an earlier study that now is an important part of the book. Seminar presentations and comments by members of the Science and Public Policy Program, especially Jerome S. Bruner, I. Bernard Cohen, Carl Kaysen, Everett I. Mendelsohn and Norman W. Storer, have been highly stimulating. Robert M. O'Clair relieved several chapters of some particularly graceless prose. Evelyn S. Lakoff had to endure not only the whims of a husband but the eccentricities of a bachelor. A small army of courageous women, among whom Kathy Jean Chernick must be cited for conspicuous heroism, labored on various drafts of the manuscript. For providing initial encouragement, we are indebted to Charles Lieber of Random House and Frederick A. Praeger. To James Murray of Prentice-Hall, we are particularly grateful.

Very special thanks must go to two distinguished statesmen of science who have themselves had a hand in guiding many of the developments described in this book. By consenting to write a foreword, James R. Killian, Jr., the first Special Assistant to the President for Science and Technology, has done us an undeserved kindness. His successor as Presidential science adviser, George B. Kistiakowsky, very graciously corrected certain misinterpretations in in the text. With all the help and cooperation we have received, our own liability for error and poor judgment is unusually heavy.

We have chosen to dedicate this book to the memory of our fathers, Maurice Dupré and Herman Lakoff, not because it has the monumental bulk frequently thought requisite for such a filial tribute, but in the belief that they would have found the problems to which it is addressed as vital and stimulating as we do. Maurice Dupré was a politician and statesman for whom public policy was much more than a bloodless abstraction. Herman Lakoff was himself a promoter of technological innovations and he was passionately concerned with politics. This book is a token of our admiration.

J. Stefan Dupré
Sanford A. Lakoff

Table of Contents

PART ONE
POLICY

1 THE REVOLUTION IN GOVERNMENT SCIENCE 3

Embryonic Science and Embryonic Government, 3; Science in the Public Service, 4; Defense and Depression, 7; The Revolution in Government Science: World War II, 9; The Revolution Consolidated: The Postwar Years, 11; The Research Partnership: Contracts and Grants, 15

2 INDUSTRY AND RESEARCH 20

The Growth of Industrial Research, 20; Some Characteristics of Industrial Research, 22; Industrial Research and the Military, 25; The New Relations of Government and Business, 30; Scientific Research and Military Needs, 34; Budgeting for R & D, 38; R & D and the Economy: The Patent Problem, 40

3 UNIVERSITIES AND GOVERNMENT 43

Government and University Research, 43; Loyalty-Security Requirements, 45; The Thorny Problem of Indirect Costs, 47; Financing Capital Facilities, 50; Sputnik and the Manpower Muddle, 52; Higher Education and Government Policy, 60

4 FORMULATING SCIENCE POLICY 64

Science and the Presidency, 65; Congress and Executive Reorganization: Proposals for a Department of Science, 69; Some Continuing Questions of Policy Organization, 73

PART TWO
POLITICS

5 ARMS AND THE SCIENTIST 81

Scientists and Warfare in the Past, 83; Between the Wars: "The Beautiful Years," 88; The Atomic Scientists and the

*Bomb, 91; Government and Atomic Research, 93; The Use of
the Bomb: First Misgivings, 96; The Curious Case of the
German Physicists, 100*

6 THE POLITICS OF DECISION 104

   *Renewal and Response, 106; The Scientist as Lobbyist, 108;
   The Scientist as Strategist, 114; A Pattern of Responsibility,
   122*

7 SECURITY IN SCIENCE 124

   *The Wartime Measures, 125; Security and the Cold War:
   Congress, 127; The Executive Follows Suit, 129; McCarthy and
   the Signal Corps Scientists, 131; The Espionage Cases, 132;
   Security in Science: Cause and Effect, 134; Security and In-
   security, 137*

8 ALIENATION AND RESPONSIBILITY 140

   *The Trial of Dr. Oppenheimer, 140; Fallout and Testing: The
   AEC and Its Critics, 150; Missiles and Space: The Politics of
   Administration, 158; PSAC: A Policy Vote for Scientists, 177*

CONCLUSION

CONCLUSION: POLICY AND POLITICS 171

   *Public and Private: The Diplomacy of Partnership, 173; Pro-
   fessional Responsibility: The Experience of the Scientists, 177;
   The Need for Public Understanding, 181*

GLOSSARY OF ABBREVIATIONS 182

PART ONE

POLICY

1

THE REVOLUTION

IN GOVERNMENT SCIENCE

Over the short span of the last two decades there has occurred a revolutionary change in the relation of government to science. During most of American history, science was regarded by government as a useful and even wholesome activity, but not as one so crucial to national security and welfare as to require constant concern and heavy subvention. Today, the situation is drastically altered. Government and science have joined in a national enterprise born of necessity and sustained by the challenges and complexities of the modern world. A brief sketch of the relations between government and science as they have evolved in American history will indicate the magnitude of this change.

Embryonic Science and Embryonic Government

At the time of the constitutional deliberations in Philadelphia, science could still be understood and even practiced by the broadly educated intellectual.[1] While Benjamin Franklin undoubtedly possessed more specialized knowledge than the others, all the Founding Fathers appreciated the potential contributions of science to the national welfare. Accordingly, the role which the projected

[1] The classic work on the development of science in government prior to 1940 is A. Hunter Dupree, *Science in the Federal Government* (Cambridge, Mass.: The Belknap Press of Harvard University Press, 1957). For an excellent shorter account, see Edwin P. Bledsoe and Harry I. Ravitz, "The Evolution of Research and Development as a Procurement Function of the Federal Government," *Research and Development Procurement Law*, Albert C. Lazure and Andrew P. Murphy, Jr., eds. (Washington, D.C.: Federal Bar Association, 1957).

federal government might play in the promotion of scientific pursuits received considerable attention and debate. If the results were meager, it was because the climate was anything but congenial. The Revolution had engendered a general distaste for powerful government. Immediately to have made the new republic a patron of the arts and sciences would have smacked too much of European monarchy. As it was, the Framers anticipated difficulties enough in winning approval for the new constitution. Furthermore, since the projected governmental system was to be federal, the functions of government were to be strictly enumerated and a large role reserved to the states. Inasmuch as the states would retain primary responsibility for education, the proposal of a large national science establishment seemed neither pressing nor appropriate.

A few suggestions were made. Charles Pinckney's constitutional plan proposed to encourage the arts, letters, and sciences by giving Congress the power to establish "seminaries" and stimulate useful inventions through rewards and immunities. Pinckney's proposal foundered on the objections of the power-conscious smaller states. James Madison proposed to empower Congress to establish a university; this too was voted down, although some delegates believed it to be implicit in the general powers granted Congress.

Only a few constitutional clauses forged specific links between the new government and science. These connections were to be found in specific grants of authority over the census, patents, and standards of weights and measures. In the long run, however, the more general powers over common defense, general welfare, and the regulation of interstate commerce were to be much more important. Indeed, the role of the federal government in science has tended to fluctuate in direct proportion to demands for these broad functions.

Science in the Public Service

Prior to the Civil War and the subsequent industrialization of America, the principal public uses made of science were of an *ad hoc* nature. The exploration and mapping of the frontier brought about the Lewis and Clark expedition and the various

Coast and Geodetic surveys. The unfortunate but prophetic experience of Ferdinand Hassler, a Coast Survey scientist, is worth at least a passing note. Hassler requested that his salary be sufficient and that he have complete control of his accounts. Shortly after, Hassler was dismissed and Congress limited the Survey to the more tractable officers of the Armed Forces.

Otherwise, public works were the principal source of demand on scientific skills; the Army Corps of Engineers together with its apprenticeship school, the U.S. Military Academy, date from 1802. For the rest, the pre-Civil War era was characterized by a low level of activity (an exception was the founding of the Smithsonian Institution at the bequest of a foreigner) and by abortive attempts to create a national university. The latter continued to founder on states' rights.

By the time of the Civil War, the scientific profession had undergone a marked transformation. Science had become highly specialized; scientists were now quite distinct from politicians and administrators. Early in the course of the War, the Navy began to make extensive use of scientific advice, setting a pattern that was to be followed more extensively in the future. Then in 1863 the National Academy of Sciences was founded by Congress at the urging of a number of scientists both in and out of government. The Academy was created as a self-perpetuating body of scientists charged with investigating various fields of science when called upon to do so by the government.

The victory of the North gave government science what was perhaps its most important stimulus to date. The "general welfare" had triumphed over "states' rights." The now freer hand of the federal government would help meet the needs of the expanding industrial system by setting up permanent scientific agencies.

The Department of Agriculture, which received its initial impetus from the Homestead and Morrill Acts of 1862, was the first and largest of these agencies. The Homestead Act promoted agricultural pursuits on the frontier lands, while the Morrill Act provided that public lands be donated to the states for the foundation of agricultural and mechanical institutions (land grant colleges). Over a period of time, the Department of Agriculture accumulated a large number of bureaus, all organized around research into particular agricultural problems (e.g., plant industry, animal industry), and received Cabinet status in 1889. Meanwhile, the Hatch Act of 1887 instituted federal support for the agricultural experiment stations that had grown up around the land grant colleges. Agricultural research was thus organized around the federal structure of the nation. Work was not limited to the Department itself; federal funds were used to sponsor research within state institutions. Agriculture therefore provides the oldest permanent example of the "extramural" government research that now permeates the American scientific establishment.

As agriculture became more specialized and productive, so did the United States become increasingly industrialized. In response to the growth of manufacturing, the spread of urbanization and the problems that accompanied these developments, the government gradually built up a number of scientifically oriented agencies designed both to provide services and to promote necessary regulations. Thus the National Bureau of Standards was set up in 1901, the Public Health Service in 1912, and the National Advisory Committee for Aeronautics in 1915. In addition, the government made considerable use of science in the administration of such regulatory legislation as the Pure Food and Drugs Act (1906). And all established bureaus grew of themselves as scientific knowledge advanced.

By the advent of World War I, the federal government made use of science on a large scale. Scientists had proved themselves to be as necessary in government as lawyers. In all federal programs, nevertheless, science was regarded not as a thing apart, valuable in itself, but always and only as a tool for the solution of problems and the formulation of policy. Concern for science, in other words, was limited to its immediate usefulness. Yet science had a wide-ranging impact on government apart from any immediate usefulness. Through regulation, it frequently provided the lead in the growing interrelation of the public and private sectors of the economy. Equally important, the need for well qualified scientists was one of the key factors in the gradual replacement of political patronage by a civil service merit system.

Defense and Depression

The outbreak of World War I in Europe in 1914 left the United States in an uncertain position. Research and development in the field of weaponry would be necessary in case of possible involvement. In 1915, the Navy called upon Thomas Edison to head a Naval Consulting Board which was divided into scientific committees (e.g., chemistry, aeronautics, ordnance, and explosives) charged with studying possible applications of science to military technology. Although the Board never realized its full potentiality because of insufficient funds, it was used in a general advisory capacity for the screening of inventions, and served as the basis for the permanent Naval Research Laboratory created after the War.

Meanwhile, the National Academy of Sciences, moribund since Civil War days, agitated for greater use of scientists by the government. Finally, President Wilson created the National Research Council as an offshoot of the Academy to help coordinate the work of scientists both in and out of government. The NRC was slow in getting started. Not until January, 1918, some eight months after America had become a belligerent, did it have so much as a central office. But there followed a brief flurry of intensive and interesting activity. The NRC, together with various divisions of the Armed Forces and such civilian agencies as the Bureau of Mines and the Bureau of Standards, embarked on extensive projects, especially in gas warfare and optics. The government established close relations with the chemical and optical industries. Because the time available was short, science became a new field of government-business cooperation and highly organized team research was carried out on an unprecedented scale. The universities too were brought into closer contact with government. They not only contributed personnel to the war effort, as in the case of the NRC, but in addition actually performed research at the government's request.

The coming of peace reduced the research establishment to its pre-war level, and the decade of the twenties saw little in the development of government science. The NRC, while given permanent status, languished for lack of funds, and Armed Forces appropriations were cut to the bone. America "kept cool" with

Coolidge, laissez-faire was restored in its full purity, and science was relegated to the proverbial ivory tower. Among high officials, only Herbert Hoover showed much interest in the scientific establishment, but his efforts to create a National Research Fund for pure science from business contributions proved a failure.

The Great Depression and the accession of Franklin D. Roosevelt to the presidency brought new activity to government science. A presidential Science Advisory Board, created in 1933, proceeded to investigate the use of science by government bureaus, and attempted to cope with the problem presented by newly unemployed scientists. In 1937, the National Resources Committee embarked on a more ambitious study of research in America. Entitled *Research—A National Resource,* the report of the Committee, issued in three parts, was a survey of science activity, not only in government, but in business and universities as well. The report noted pointedly that while some universities spent as much as 25 per cent of their income on research and certain business firms as much as 4 per cent of their gross income, the government devoted only about 2 per cent of its budget to science.[2] Considerable attention was devoted to past contributions of research to the national economy. Economic benefits derived from the application of scientific knowledge in the chemical, petroleum, electrical, rubber, metal, and pharmaceutical industries were discussed in some detail. It was clearly implied that discoveries made possible by sponsored research might provide the stimulus needed by the national economy.

At about the time the report was published, soundings by economists were reaching new depths of pessimism over America's long-run economic prospects. The frontier was settled, and such major technological discoveries as steam power and internal combustion had been exploited. In the absence of such vast opportunities for investment, and faced with slower population growth, the "mature" American economy appeared doomed to "stagnation," i.e., chronic unemployment coupled with an absence of economic growth. In this bleak atmosphere, the report offered a ray of hope. Scientific research might now create investment opportunities and help restore prosperity. The Committee recommended that the federal

---

[2] National Resources Committee, *Research—A National Resource* (Washington, D.C.: Government Printing Office, 1938), I, 3.

government establish closer relations with scientists in private life and sponsor more research both within and outside its own establishment. But farsighted as they were, little did the authors of *Research—A National Resource* realize the sweeping changes that war would bring.

The Revolution in Government Science: World War II

World War II radically altered the hitherto casual relation of science to American government. In 1939, government agencies continued to use science as a tool, for *ad hoc* technical needs only. Governmental research, with the exception of the Department of Agriculture and its state experimental stations, was centered almost entirely in agency laboratories proper. The federal budget alloted about $50 million per year to research.[3] Today, the federal government spends almost ten *billion* dollars on research and development, of which over three-quarters is not performed by the government at all but by industry, universities, and various nonprofit institutions. In two decades an organizational revolution has taken place, based on the scientific developments of the Second World War.

As the Nazi *Blitzkrieg* demonstrated the efficacy of new techniques and improved weapons, the American government turned to the scientific community for help in the event of involvement. Accordingly, President Roosevelt established a National Defense Research Committee in 1940 to support and coordinate research on weapons. Unlike the National Research Council in World War I, the NDRC was to receive generous support. Vannevar Bush, President of the Carnegie Institution, was Chairman, and members included the presidents of Harvard and M.I.T., the U.S. Commissioner of Patents, the president of Bell Telephone Laboratories, an Army general, an admiral, and two practicing university scientists. Thus government agencies, both civilian and military, and industry, universities, and nonprofit institutions as well, were all represented. It was evident that they would have to pool resources. There was not time to transfer personnel and facilities to the

---

[3] The President's Scientific Research Board, *Science and Public Policy* (Washington, D.C.: Government Printing Office, 1947), I, 10.

government. The war effort demanded the use of established institutions in a major enterprise of scientific cooperation.

NDRC was the first step toward an increased and better coordinated national research effort. The Committee not only studied problems presented by the military, but also pursued research projects of its own choosing.

Before long, however, the need became clear not only to pursue scientific research in the strict sense, but also to develop research findings into working models that would make weapons production possible. In order to fulfill these needs, President Roosevelt formed the Office of Scientific Research and Development in 1941 by executive order, and attached it to the Executive Office of the President. Headed by the ubiquitous Vannevar Bush, OSRD served as a clearinghouse for much of the R & D—research and development (engineering work)—of the Army, the Navy, the National Advisory Committee for Aeronautics, and NDRC. OSRD could also initiate whatever R & D projects it deemed promising, and served as a mobilization center for scientific manpower. Thus, to take the leading example, OSRD began the atomic energy research program, passing it on to the Army's Manhattan Project only in 1943 when much of the R & D had been done, and retained substantial connection with the work thereafter.

As the wartime scientific effort progressed, a number of important organizational features emerged. Through Vannevar Bush's position as head of a branch of the Executive Office of the President, science gained unprecedented access to the chief executive. NDRC, NACA, and the Armed Forces made use of scientific advisory committees on an extensive scale. This was especially true of NDRC, which had over fifty committees on everything from Aviation Breathing Equipment to Unrotated Projectile Propellants. As closer research connections drew government, business, and universities together, the government adopted new contractual devices to provide a legal framework for the R & D relationship. The government used contracts not only to procure specific pieces of research; it also employed them to set up entire research centers. These centers were to be financed by government funds and administered by industry and universities. For example, the Los Alamos Laboratory (of atomic bomb fame) was set up by an Army contract with the University of California. Practically overnight, the government had created a national research enterprise.[4]

The success of this enormous organizational scheme and of the scientists who composed it introduced the American people to a new era of costly and important scientific developments. The public was at once titillated and terrified by advances made during the War. Popular interest in science reached an unprecedented peak and pressure built up for the use of scientific creativity for peacetime purposes. Science itself had developed some new fields, such as atomic energy, and in many instances the advances made brought a new cost structure to research. Nuclear accelerators, modern wind tunnels, and the like are tremendously expensive pieces of equipment. These higher costs meant that research would require peacetime monetary support at an unprecedented level. Finally there were the scientists themselves, whose ivory towers lay shattered. Nearly all had been connected with government work in one fashion or another. Because their work was now more expensive, they formed a pressure group for more generous government help, especially in the heretofore generally neglected area of basic research. In addition, after spending the War in a status of quasimobilization, they understandably pressed for greater freedom and as much control over the scientific establishment as possible.

The Revolution Consolidated: The Postwar Years

The first important document to embody some of the thinking of the scientists was a report to the President by Vannevar Bush entitled *Science, The Endless Frontier*, issued in July, 1945. Bush stressed the importance of research for national security and for the advancement of medicine. As to the economic benefits to be derived from scientific activity he wrote:

> One of our hopes is that after the war there will be full employment. To reach that goal the full creative and productive energies of the American people must be released. To create more jobs we must

[4] For an excellent account of the wartime organization of scientific research, see Irvin Stewart, *Organizing Scientific Research for War* (Boston: Atlantic, Little Brown & Co., 1948).

make new and better and cheaper products. We want plenty of new, vigorous enterprises. But new products and processes are not born full-grown. They are founded on new principles and new conceptions which in turn result from basic scientific research. Basic scientific research is scientific capital. Moreover, we cannot any longer depend upon Europe as a major source of this scientific capital. Clearly, more and better scientific research is one essential to the achievement of our goal of full employment.[5]

Here was the argument that had been implicit in the National Resources Committee's *Research—A National Resource*. The challenge of the Axis Powers had cured the Great Depression, but systematic investigation would now be necessary for a peacetime economy whose state of technological advancement was such that innovation could only result from intensive groundwork in science. Bush recommended that a special government agency be set up to foster basic research and encourage the development of scientific manpower. This recommendation was heartily supported in *Science and Public Policy*, a report made two years later by the President's Scientific Research Board, chaired by John R. Steelman. In addition, the Steelman Report urged that the government spend at least one per cent of the gross national product on research and development and that it support basic research in universities and nonprofit institutions to the extent of $250 million by 1957.[6]

As these recommendations were being made, a full-blown debate emerged over the new organizational direction of the postwar scientific establishment. An important phase of this debate accompanied the founding of the Atomic Energy Commission. It concerned the proposed Commission's relations to Congress and the executive, the extent of military and civilian control, and the role of private enterprise in the development of atomic energy. As created in 1946, the AEC was headed by civilian commissioners responsible to the President but appointed for fixed terms and authorized to control all nuclear research, development, and production.

In the case of the National Science Foundation, which was to

---

[5] Vannevar Bush, *Science, The Endless Frontier* (Washington, D.C.: Government Printing Office, 1945), p. 2.

[6] The President's Scientific Research Board, *Science and Public Policy*, I, 6.

implement the recommendations for basic research support made in the Bush and Steelman Reports, controversy raged over the relation of the proposed agency to the presidency. Should it be headed by an independent group of part-time scientist-commissioners or by an administrator appointed by the President? After five years of debate, the NSF finally emerged in 1950 with a presidentially appointed director and a board of part-time scientists with veto power over the award of research grants.

Fortunately, basic research was not left without means of government support during the long period involved in the creation of NSF. The Office of Naval Research embarked on a major effort to foster university work. And the National Institutes of Health, the research branch of the Public Health Service, launched a rapidly growing program of support for research in the medical sciences.

By 1950, science had found a lasting place as an important adjunct to the national quest for general welfare and economic progress. But with the advent of the Korean conflict and the intensification of the Cold War, government once again increased the military orientation of its research and development. Then the shock of the Sputnik crisis in 1957 occasioned another great debate and resulted in a new flurry of activity. Efforts to bring greater flexibility to military research led to the formation of an Advanced Research Projects Agency in the Department of Defense. President Eisenhower gave to scientists important advisory posts within the White House, and Congress created a new independent agency, the National Aeronautics and Space Administration, to take over from the old National Advisory Committee for Aeronautics and carry out research on space with civilian significance.

Since Sputnik, government spending on research and development programs has increased about $4 billion, and scientific manpower programs have received fresh attention. The government now spends far greater amounts for research than the postwar Bush and Steelman Reports envisaged. A statistical summary of financial expenditure as it was estimated in 1960 appears in Table I. Two obvious facts emerge from the figures. The first is that the Department of Defense and the defense-oriented civilian agencies spend the overwhelmingly predominant part of the nation's research and development budget. Second, and most important, the majority of

TABLE I

TOTAL FEDERAL GOVERNMENT OBLIGATIONS FOR CONDUCT OF RESEARCH AND DEVELOPMENT, FISCAL 1960 *

As Estimated in *The Budget*, 1960—Reflecting Congressional Action

(Dollar figures in millions)

	Total		Intramural**		Extramural †	
TOTAL	$8,022.3	100.0%	$1,842.4	100.0%	$6,179.9	100.0%
Department of the Air Force	3,013.1	37.6	404.2	21.9	2,608.9	42.2
Department of the Navy	1,461.0	18.2	441.0	23.9	1,020.0	16.5
Department of the Army	1,181.3	14.7	417.6	22.7	763.7	12.4
Other Dept. of Defense	417.9	5.2	43.0	2.3	374.9	6.1
Atomic Energy Commission	790.5	9.9	12.2	0.7	778.3	12.6
National Aeronautics and Space Administration	424.9	5.3	229.5	12.5	195.4	3.2
Department of Health, Education & Welfare (including National Institutes of Health)	321.6	4.0	87.9	4.8	233.7	3.8
Department of Agriculture	144.0	1.8	89.9	4.9	54.1	0.9
National Science Foundation	72.2	0.9	5.3	0.3	66.9	1.1
Department of the Interior	67.9	0.8	57.2	3.1	10.7	0.2
Federal Aviation Agency	51.5	0.6	7.5	0.4	44.0	0.7
Department of Commerce	32.4	0.4	23.2	1.3	9.2	0.1
Miscellaneous	44.0	0.5	23.9	1.3	20.1	0.3

* Source: National Science Foundation, *Federal Funds for Science IX* (Washington, D.C.: Government Printing Office, 1960). Figures may not add to totals because of rounding.

** Intramural research is carried on within government laboratories.

† Extramural research is carried out by contract or grant in industry, universities, research centers under their management, or independent laboratories.

the R & D work is not performed within the government at all but elsewhere, in business, universities and nonprofit institutions. This development, more than anything else, indicates the nature of the revolution in government finance. The traditional distinctions among government, industry, and education have been drastically altered in favor of a partnership based on the national need for research.

The Research Partnership: Contracts and Grants

The character of the research partnership among government, business, and universities has been closely affected by the legal devices through which government procures and supports extramural R & D. These devices provide the basis of the new system of interdependence between government and private institutions. They have also been the focus of numerous problems arising from this novel relationship. We shall confine ourselves for the moment to the broad evolution of these legal instruments from the government's point of view. There are two devices: the contract and the grant, of which the contract has been by far the more important.[7]

The contract is a very old adjunct of day-to-day government. The United States has always used contracts as a common device to procure goods and services from business. Such goods and services have traditionally been of a very mundane sort: the construction and maintenance of buildings, Armed Forces supplies, office equipment, and the like. Since procurement of this type is a source of money to private enterprise, the government early took steps to ensure that competition for this business would be equitable and that the desired items would be acquired at minimum cost to the public treasury. As early as 1809, Congress passed a law requiring open advertising in all government contracts. By the terms of the law government agencies were required to specify their needs exactly and publicize them before the business community at large. All interested firms could then submit bids quoting the exact prices for supplying the desired items. The agency would then publicly open the bids and normally award the contract to the responsible firm ready to meet the advertised specifications for the lowest price.

A contract of this type, which is generally known as an advertised

[7] For useful historical background on the development of contracting procedures, see Department of Defense, *Procurement Presentation to the Procurement Subcommittee of the Committee on Armed Services, United States Senate* (Washington, D.C.: Government Printing Office, 1960).

fixed price contract, has often been little more than an ideal in government procurement. The government has chosen to deviate from the model on numerous occasions, particularly in times of emergency. But only recently has Congress explicitly recognized that deviations from the model are a permanent fixture in government contracting. Scientific research was primarily responsible for this step.

The advertised fixed price contract is not designed for the procurement of research services. Open advertising requires that the government have exact prior knowledge of the item it wishes to procure and that the item in question be sufficiently standardized to enable a large number of firms to compete. Research, on the other hand, is purchased because the government does not know precisely what it wants. Therefore, there can be no question of precise specifications; at best the government can indicate only the broad area of investigation. Research is also highly specialized, requiring very scarce combinations of scientific talent and physical facilities. Indeed, because of his professional expertise, the potential contractor may have a larger part than the government in determining the kinds of research required. Thus the government must search carefully for potential contractors and determine with them the nature of the work to be done, a process further complicated by the requirement of secrecy.

Because of these problems, it has become imperative that the government let its research contracts through negotiation rather than by open advertisement. Moreover, the uncertainty involved in research has forced a change in the most traditional principle of contracting—the method of determining the price of the item to be procured. Under the fixed price contract, the contractor is bound to provide the specified items for the price quoted in his bid. But he must have some experience with the production of the items concerned in order to submit a realistic bid. The uncertainty that surrounds research makes such precise price determination impossible. The government has therefore instituted cost-reimbursement contracts, under which it simply reimburses all costs incurred by the contractor, whatever their level. Government contracting has thus been seriously modified by the research and development effort. Instead of calling for maximum competition and rigid, minimum prices, the government negotiates the work to be done with a limited number of firms and reimburses all reasonable costs regardless of amount.

This great change was formally sanctioned by Congress in the First War Powers Act of 1941 which released government agencies engaged in the war effort from the traditional contracting procedures. Since the new arrangements were made permanent at the end of the War, the government has been able to enter into negotiated cost-reimbursement contracts whenever necessary.

Government agencies have used the new contracting powers not only for the procurement of specific pieces of research and development but also for more general purposes. Early in the War, cost-reimbursement contracts provided the legal basis for entire institutions. The Los Alamos Laboratory, the offspring of an Army contract with the University of California, called for the reimbursement of all costs incurred in setting up the laboratory and in financing its research performance. Since the War, Los Alamos has passed under the aegis of the Atomic Energy Commission. Through the continuing arrangements, Los Alamos remains under the broad administrative supervision of the University of California and receives all its financial support from the government. Over thirty other research centers are similarly supported by cost contracts between government agencies and business or universities. Such large contracts are broad, administrative "master" contracts entailing wide discretion on the part of the research center in the selection of projects and personnel.

Government has further developed contractual procedure to embrace ever larger projects. In the single manager weapons-system contracts, one of a variety of contracts pioneered by the Air Force, responsibility for the research, development, testing, evaluation, and production of an entire weapon such as the B-52 or the B-70 is vested in a business firm through a series of "prime" contracts all of which, except for production, are of the cost-reimbursement variety. The prime contractor then lets out numerous subcontracts for component parts of the weapon and assumes responsibility for the final integration of all components into a complete weapon.

Contracting has thus proved to be a highly flexible tool in helping to mold a national research establishment. In the key area of basic research or pure science, contracts have been further modified, indeed transformed, into a second type of legal device known as a grant. By the very nature of basic research, goals are so indefinite and procedures so vague that maximum freedom is necessary to enable the researcher to perform his task. After the War, numerous complaints were heard from within the scientific community because of the administrative chores involved in handling government contracts. Not only do contracts require frequent financial and progress reports, but contracting officers have actual administrative responsibilities and must oversee and authorize equipment purchases and the like. Until the creation of the National Science Foundation, the strictness of contractual conditions was somewhat mitigated through administrative discretion; many of the more bothersome requirements were ignored. But the situation was clarified when NSF was authorized to make grants rather than contracts.

Government grants are patterned in part on private foundation grants. They have few reporting requirements, give the grantee very broad discretion, and allow the grantee to retain title in the facilities purchased with the funds. Until 1957, NSF, together with the National Institutes of Health which had received prior authority, was the only government agency supporting basic research through grants. But in that year Congress authorized all other agencies to make grants instead of contracts where appropriate, thereby giving them still greater flexibility in the procurement of extramural research.

Extramural government research is the distinguishing characteristic of organized science in America. It is based on a contractual system initially developed during World War II. At that time, pressure for quick results and the existing distribution of personnel and facilities left the government with no alternative other than to make contracts with established private institutions.

The continuation and indeed the expansion of contractual research in the postwar era are due both to necessity and to convenience. The government has found that scientists, especially those in universities, are closely attached to their institutions. As to scientists in business, contracting has enabled the government to meet industrial salary scales because civil service pay regulations do not apply to contractors' employees. Contracting also has the advantage of flexibility; it makes scientists and laboratories anywhere in the nation available for government programs. For these reasons, the government, rather than greatly expanding its own internal science organization, has continued to finance outside performance of research.

Once established, an extended program of extramural research has built-in factors tending to reinforce it. As large sums of federal money have poured into business and universities, these institutions have gradually adapted themselves to the presence of public support and have come in many instances to depend upon it and press for it. Finally, the system of extramural research, because it involves close public and private cooperation, responds to a general American concern for limited government and external participation. But a research partnership between public and private institutions does not necessarily work easily and automatically. In order to perform its tasks effectively, it must be the object of thoughtfully constructed policies and of mutual accommodation between the partners. Its smooth functioning is a major organizational challenge.

2

Industry and Research

In terms of sheer size, industrial research and development, the majority of it financed by the government, dominates the American science establishment. Expenditure for R & D performed by business accounts for over three-quarters of all R & D spending in the nation. In 1959, the total cost of industrial R & D was $9.4 billion, of which $5.4 billion or 57 per cent was contributed through federal contracts.[1]

The over-all size of this partnership in dollar terms is impressive in itself. But even more important is the nature of the links that R & D has forged between public and private interests. Since the bulk of military R & D is performed by industry, business has become an integral part of defense planning and strategy. At the same time, industrial research can have a vital influence on economic growth, which is increasingly becoming a public concern. Finally, because industrial R & D tends to enhance the position of large firms, the government finds itself in the anomalous position of supporting oligopoly through its research procurement while maintaining its traditional concern for free competition.

The Growth of Industrial Research

Business firms have always been closely concerned with what Joseph A. Schumpeter, the economist, called innovation, i.e., the marketing of inventions either in the form of new goods or of new processes of manufacture. Whereas inventions in the nineteenth

[1] National Science Foundation, *Funds for Research and Development in Industry* (Washington, D.C.: Government Printing Office, 1960), p. 7.

century often stemmed more from the inventor's ingenuity than from his knowledge of scientific principles, systematic scientific research became necessary both because of the accumulation of knowledge and because of the technological complexity that has accompanied progress. Industrial research is a child of the twentieth century, born of the marriage of science and technology.

In the United States, science first entered business in the electrical industry that sprang from the work of Thomas Edison and others, and in the textile and chemical industries. Research quickly spread to nearly all other manufacturing industries both old and new, and also to nonmanufacturing ones (e.g., telecommunications and broadcasting). Many new industries, such as electronics, are inherently research-oriented, but even those not characterized by constant innovation, such as the automobile industry, maintain research laboratories.

The following table gives a rough statistical picture of the growth of industrial research.

TABLE II

GROWTH OF INDUSTRIAL RESEARCH, 1921-1957 *

	1921	1940	1953	1957
R & D expenditure in millions of dollars	29	234	3,400	7,200
Scientists and engineers employed in R & D	9,000	60,000	554,000	728,000

* Sources: National Research Council, National Resources Committee, National Science Foundation. Since the data were collected by varying techniques for each of the years shown, they are offered only as a very rough approximation of historical development.

From 1921 to 1957 dollar expenditure for industrial R & D increased from a few millions to several billions and the number of scientists and engineers employed by business grew from under ten thousand to almost three-quarters of a million. Especially significant is the fact that while the number of research employees increased 550 per cent in the two decades between 1921 and 1940, an increase of over 800 per cent was recorded in the seventeen years from 1940 to 1957.

Some Characteristics of Industrial Research

Heavy business expenditure on science and engineering is founded on eminently practical considerations. Its most important long run goal is, of course, innovation, the discovery of a new product, of new processes of production, or of new uses for an existing product. But business research serves more immediate purposes as well; it can help reduce production costs, eliminate troubles that may develop in a product, or make small modifications that will increase the appeal of a product to prospective purchasers. All these functions serve both the profit motive and the competitive position of the business firm. To a certain extent, industrial research is also used increasingly to promote the intangible asset of consumer "good will." In Jacob Schmookler's words,

> One of Madison Avenue's favorite devices these days is to use a wise and benign-looking man in a laboratory smock to present "the latest research findings." The admen thus capitalize on the public's belief in the ability of science to solve its problems, and help generate the notion that private enterprise wages unceasing battle to make science serve the public good.[2]

The extent of business research varies widely according to the type of industry and the size of a company. The statistics presented in Table III, which are the result of a 1956 National Science Foundation survey, will give the reader an idea of business spending on R & D in the major categories of industry by business firms of various size. Approximately one-half the expenditure shown in the table can be attributed to federal government contracts.

The most research-oriented industries in the United States are those concerned with aircraft and electrical equipment. They are also the ones whose research is most heavily financed by the government. Over 85 per cent of the cost of R & D in the aircraft industry is covered by federal contracts, as is almost two-thirds of R & D in the electronics industry. Together with the chemicals and machinery industries, whose R & D is not as heavily financed

[2] Jacob Schmookler, "Technological Progress and the Modern American Corporation," *The Corporation in Modern Society*, Edward S. Mason, ed. (Cambridge, Mass.: Harvard University Press, 1959), p. 141.

Table III

COST OF RESEARCH AND DEVELOPMENT, BY SIZE
OF COMPANY AND INDUSTRY, 1956 *
(In millions of dollars)

Industry	All Companies	Companies with total employment of:				
		8-99	100-499	500-999	1000-4999	5000 or more
All industries	$6,230.9	165.3	307.6	174.8	631.2	4,952.0
Food and other kindred products	75.9	2.9	3.9	2.2	9.4	57.5
Chemicals & allied products	511.7	25.5	36.9	28.5	89.9	331.0
Petroleum products & extraction	200.9	5.7	2.6	**	43.2	149.3
Rubber products	82.4	1.3	2.8	1.3	6.7	70.3
Primary metal industries	87.9	4.4	5.9	1.3	15.7	60.6
Fabricated metal products & ordnance	175.7	14.8	29.6	13.4	50.4	67.4
Machinery	610.6	41.1	48.7	18.5	74.3	427.9
Electrical equipment	1,038.0	17.8	102.5	56.9	110.1	750.8
Aircraft and parts	2,078.7	2.3	11.2	6.1	48.4	2,010.7
Professional and scientific instruments	221.1	6.0	9.7	17.6	63.4	124.5
Other manufacturing industries	869.7	32.5	36.3	16.8	71.2	713.0
Nonmanufacturing industries	278.2	11.0	17.5	12.0	48.4	189.3

* Source: National Science Foundation, *Science and Engineering in American Industry*, November 1959.
** Insufficient data.

by the government, aircraft and electronics account for 60 per cent of all spending on industrial R & D.

The concentration of R & D is a striking characteristic of America's contemporary industrial structure. Of the total funds spent on industrial R & D in 1956, 79.5 per cent was expended by firms with over 5,000 employees, 89.6 per cent by firms with over 1,000 employees. Among the several industries, the most research-oriented, the aircraft industry, was most marked by concentration. In 1956, 96.7 per cent of total aircraft research expenditure was made by firms with over 5,000 employees. While the electronics industry has spawned a number of small "glamor" firms that constitute a speculator's delight, it was also marked by high concentration: in 1956 firms with over 5,000 employees performed 72.3 per cent of the R & D.

Joseph Schumpeter not only predicted the growing dependence of business on systematic research for innovation, but he also foresaw the increasing dominance of the large firm. Concentration would occur, he believed, in large part because of the ability of big business to finance research.[3]

The money a business firm spends internally on research must come from profits. These profits can be used otherwise either for dividends or for internal investment in existing capital equipment. Since a firm will always seek additional profits, funds expended on research are expected to pay off in the long run. Internally financed R & D thus takes on the nature of a speculative investment. A frequent business policy is to allocate a fixed percentage of annual gross sales or gross receipts to research. The large firm therefore enjoys a decisive advantage over the smaller firm because of its larger volume of sales and receipts. This means that it can afford better research facilities and a greater quantity of diversified research projects. Again, because of the greater volume of research investment, the large firm's need for short-run pay-off from individual projects is smaller. Hence there is reduced pressure on industrial research personnel and greater freedom in the choice of projects. Interestingly enough, the working atmosphere thus generated has often proved to be the one most conducive to major research "breakthroughs."

The trend in favor of big business research is self-reinforcing. Because of their excellent facilities and relaxed working atmosphere, large firms can attract scientific talent of a very high caliber. The acquisition of good scientists in large numbers makes possible the recruitment of still further talent; scientists are attracted by the possibilities of professional intercourse with colleagues of high repute. It is thus no accident that the two industrial laboratories regarded as the best in America are the offspring of major firms—the Bell Telephone Laboratories and the General Electric Laboratories.

The introduction of government funds into the industrial research picture only serves to strengthen existing trends toward concentration. When federal agencies wish to purchase R & D findings, they will naturally turn to the large firms whose technical and

[3] See especially his brilliant *Capitalism, Socialism and Democracy*, 3rd ed. (New York: Harper & Brothers, 1950).

personnel capabilities offer the greatest promise of effective results. The government therefore occupies an uncomfortable and anomalous position. While antitrust legislation has made the promotion of competition and the prevention of monopoly traditional concerns of public policy, the government's new research needs actually promote trends in the opposite direction.

Industrial Research and the Military

Government-business relations in R & D are based overwhelmingly on the military needs of the nation. The Armed Forces, together with two defense-related agencies, the Atomic Energy Commission and the National Aeronautics and Space Administration, account for 99 per cent of the public funds that go into industrial R & D, and finance fully one-half of total business research.

Weapons have become so complex that research cannot easily be separated from production. The advancement of contemporary military technology depends on research in all its phases. From the findings of basic research, the business firm engages in what is commonly called "applied research," attempting to translate scientific principles into a workable device such as an airfoil or a tube. The work progresses into technical or component development when attempts are made to modify and combine the devices found through applied research into a piece of military equipment such as an engine. Next comes system development, in which the goal is to assemble the components worked out in technical development into a whole weapon in prototype form. The prototype is then tested, and only subsequently does full-scale production begin. Production itself involves extensive development of machine tools, and in its initial stages may require important modifications in the prototype.

Scientific research and engineering development thus pervade the entire process of modern weapons production. In such advanced systems as aircraft and missiles virtually no components are standardized; even the smallest item is usually the result of an individual R & D project. Moreover, constant feedback into early phases of R & D is common; when a weapon reaches the production stage, it is often necessary to perform further research in order to make necessary modifications in a component.

Business firms that engage in defense production must have considerable research capacity. In addition they have had to develop highly specialized managerial ability in order to integrate R & D findings into working components and actual weapons. Our present defense industry is no longer one in which business acts as a simple supplier of standard weapons to the government. Instead, government purchases scientific skills, management, and production in a package. Three examples will help to articulate the new connections that our advanced defense technology has forged between business and government: the Sandia Corporation, the NIKE missile, and the B-70 bomber.

Special Research Centers: The Sandia Corporation. The Sandia Corporation is an example of a company-managed institution created and financed solely by government funds to carry out continuing R & D on broad scientific problems.[4] It specializes in R & D on atomic weapons. Sandia was originally attached to the famous Los Alamos Laboratory. As Sandia's A-bomb research expanded, the University of California, over-all manager of both Los Alamos and Sandia, decided to drop Sandia because its work was not deemed sufficiently theoretical to warrant a university connection. The Atomic Energy Commission thereupon looked elsewhere for a contractor and selected the Western Electric Company, the manufacturing arm of the Bell System. A cost-reimbursement contract was then concluded between the AEC and Western Electric covering R & D on ordnance aspects of atomic weapons and transferring Sandia to that company.

Under the terms of the contract, Sandia's management is subject to Western Electric, which in turn is responsible to the government for its operations. The AEC's regional headquarters, the Albuquerque Operations Office, has rights of inspection and must be consulted on certain matters of policy. Sandia's projects are carried out at the request or with the approval of the AEC. Its annual budget is formulated on the basis of current project requirements and

---

[4] For an interesting account of Sandia's management, see Kimball Prince, "Sandia Corporation: A Science-Industry-Government Approach to Management of a Special Project," *Research and Development Procurement Law,* pp. 432-443.

submitted to the AEC Finance Division. After AEC approval has been secured, Sandia's budget becomes a part of the Congressional AEC appropriations bills. Its capital facilities are constructed under AEC contracts and are wholly owned by the government.

Sandia's relationship with its parent company has been especially important in the matter of scientific and managerial personnel. Sandia has drawn a number of high level scientists and executives from the Bell System. In its responsibility for Sandia the Bell System can be considered to perform a public function. The parent company derives no profit from the operation, and has no financial stake in it. The AEC, meanwhile, benefits from the work performed by Sandia under business freedom from civil service and similar government regulations. Some sixteen institutions like Sandia have emerged from similar arrangements between government and business. They all operate in a semiautonomous fashion, attached loosely to business firms and financed entirely by public money.

Joint Performance of R & D: The NIKE Missile. The bulk of military R & D is not conducted in separate institutions like Sandia but directly by business firms. Frequently, a large company and a government agency will jointly undertake the development of a complex weapon, as in the case of the NIKE missile, now a standard antiaircraft weapon.[5]

The possibility of an antiaircraft missile was originally conceived within the United States Army at the close of World War II. The Army Ordnance Corps thereupon set to work on the missile, using such facilities as its Frankford Arsenal. Simultaneously, the Ordnance Corps entered into negotiation with industry. It selected the Western Electric Company as contractor on a cost-plus-fixed-fee basis; the government was to reimburse all costs and pay a fixed fee in lieu of profit. To supervise the work, the Ordnance Corps appointed a Contracting Officer who settled in New York, the location of Western Electric's head office. He was authorized to approve all major aspects of expenditure under the contract.

As the NIKE progressed, Western Electric, with Army approval, subcontracted portions of the work to other firms. Subordinate contracting officers were appointed by the Ordnance Corps to supervise

[5] See James J. Kelly, "The Birth of a Missile—Legal and Contractual Aspects," *Research and Development Procurement Law*, pp. 420-431.

the subcontractors. Buildings and other facilities required by the contractor and subcontractors were constructed with government money.

In addition to the business firms, the Army made extensive use of its own facilities, notably the Frankford and Redstone Arsenals, and the White Sands Proving Ground. Concurrently, the Army undertook the preparation of NIKE launching sites, most of them located near major U.S. cities. After extensive testing of the prototype missile, the Army awarded Western Electric the production contract. This contract was made on a fixed price basis.

Through the experience gained in the production of the original NIKE, the Army and Western Electric subsequently made plans for an improved version. A cost-plus-fixed-fee contract was let to Western Electric for further R & D work, and the cycle was resumed, resulting in the more advanced NIKE-Hercules.

The NIKE is an excellent example of contractual cooperation between business and government. Both Western Electric and the Army shared in the performance of the work; Army contracting officers supervised the portion conducted by Western Electric and its subcontractors. Close relations between government and business personnel were maintained throughout.

"Weapons-System Management": The B-70. The Army-sponsored NIKE features relatively heavy government participation both in management and R & D. But greater reliance for over-all management and work performance can and has been placed on business. In this regard the Air Force, as the newest branch of the Armed Services with fewer facilities of its own, has been the pioneer. The "weapons-system management" concept places sole responsibility for the research, development, integration, and production of a complete weapon in a prime contractor under only the most general kind of supervision. The B-70, a supersonic bomber presently in development, is a case in point.[6]

In 1954, the Air Force, having formulated general operating requirements for such a bomber, invited six aircraft companies to

[6] An elaborate discussion of weapons-system contracting is to be found in J. Stefan Dupré and W. Eric Gustafson, "The New Public Administration: Problems and Benefits for the Contractor in Government by Contract," Paper presented at the 1960 Annual Meeting of the American Political Science Association.

submit designs and proposals. The companies, all well-known firms, included North American Aviation, the Boeing Airplane Company, and Convair. After over two years of competition and independent evaluations by the Air Research and Development Command, the Air Materiel Command, and the Strategic Air Command, the design proposed by North American was declared the winner. The Air Force designated North American to be the weapons-system prime contractor and awarded what has come to be known as a Phase I contract authorizing further design work and construction mockups. The Phase I contract is on a cost-plus-fixed-fee (CPFF) basis. Normally this initial contract will be followed by a Phase II contract (usually CPFF) for completion of engineering and construction of prototypes, and finally a Phase III contract for production.

In awarding the prime contract to North American, the Air Force was not primarily concerned with costs. More important were the nature of North American's design, the technical analysis of the problems involved in developing the B-70, and the evaluation of the company's engineering, management, and production capabilities. Complete estimates of costs were of course submitted. It is on these estimates, or "target costs," that the fixed fee is based, in the case of the B-70, $6\frac{1}{2}$ per cent.

As prime contractor, North American received full responsibility for the letting of subcontracts, subject to Air Force approval, on a CPFF basis. In the case of each main subcontract (referred to as a first tier subcontract), North American compiled a list of qualified bidders which was submitted to the Air Force for approval. North American then sent invitations to bid to the listed firms, held conferences with prospective bidders and made on-site evaluations of the bidders' plants. North American assessed all bids and awarded subcontracts with Air Force approval.

The only component of the B-70 not being developed under the direct supervision of North American is the engine, for which General Electric is "associate contractor," holding a contract directly from the Air Force and reporting to the government except for certain aspects of technical coordination on which it has liaison with North American.

In each subcontracting plant, North American maintains a resi-

dent representative charged with coordination and other supervision. All subcontractors must submit monthly progress and cost
reports. Thus as prime contractor, North American essentially takes
the place that might otherwise be occupied by Air Force personnel.

Each subcontractor himself enters into contracts with a second
tier of subcontractors. Similar contracts can be let through third-
and fourth-tier subcontractors. The main consideration in all cases
is the managerial and technical capabilities of the firm. Supervisory
and administrative responsibilities are assumed by each tier of
subcontractors in relation to the next lower tier. In this manner,
weapons-system contracting is a situation in which business assumes
the major responsibility for research, production, and administration. Government merely stands by to offer very general supervision.

The New Relations of Government and Business

Government procurement of complex weapons like NIKE and
the B-70 involves a conception of business that goes far beyond
the traditional operation of the industrial firm in a market setting.
In order to appreciate the change, we must return to the operation
of the advertised fixed price contracts. Here a firm, having secured
a contract competitively by offering the lowest price, thereupon
assumes all the risks involved in producing the desired item. If its
actual costs turn out to be higher than those quoted in its bid, it
assumes the whole burden of the loss. Conversely, should its actual
costs be lower than originally estimated, it reaps all resulting profits.
The advertised fixed price contract thus brings the full forces of the
market to bear on the contractor.

By contrast, the negotiated cost-plus-fixed-fee contract by-passes
the market mechanism. Competition is restricted to those firms with
whom negotiation takes place. This competition is based on technical and managerial capabilities rather than on price. Because the
government stands ready to reimburse all reasonable costs and to
provide necessary capital equipment, the firm assumes no financial
risk. Indeed government, rather than business, assumes the role of
entrepreneur.

Finally, since a firm's fixed fee is guaranteed, it has no economic
incentive to hold costs to a minimum. The government has made

some effort to restore cost-reducing incentives with *cost-plus-incen-tive-fee* and *fixed-price-incentive-fee* contracts for use in late phases of development and early phases of production.* These contracts enable business to share in savings that reduce costs below established targets. But they do not prevent firms from negotiating for high target costs; indeed they encourage them to do so. Hence cost control now depends on administrative checks rather than on the market mechanism.

The administered incentives for cost control are deployed by three arms of the government. These are the contracting agency (Army, Navy, Air Force, AEC, and so on), the Congressional Committee, and the General Accounting Office, the watchdog agency of the Congress. The contracting agency is the most directly responsible for administration. It appoints contracting officers, receives frequent cost reports from the contractor, and conducts audits of the contractor's books. But it remains in a difficult position vis-à-vis business, especially in the negotiation of target costs. Since experience with thousands of cost components is necessary in these negotiations, business is bound to hold advantages over representatives of a government agency. Furthermore, close personal ties may at times exist between business and government negotiators.

Particularly disturbing to Congress has been the growing propensity of business firms engaged in defense work to hire ex-Armed Services personnel. Table IV gives a breakdown of the number of retired military officers and retired flag and general officers employed by the ten largest defense contractors in 1959. The number is impressive in all cases except American Telephone and Telegraph (which interestingly enough holds a highly privileged market position) and is exceptional in the General Dynamics and Lockheed Corporations. The employment of retired officers may have some distinct advantages to the business firm in securing defense contracts. As a recent Congressional Report points out, "The 'coincidence' of contracts and personal contacts with firms represented by retired officers and retired civilian officials sometimes

---

* A *cost-plus-incentive-fee* contract assures the contractor a fixed fee which can be increased if he performs his task for less than the target cost. The *fixed-price-incentive-fee* contract, while placing a firm ceiling on costs, allows savings below the estimated costs to be shared between the government and the contractor.

TABLE IV

EMPLOYMENT OF RETIRED MILITARY OFFICERS BY TEN
LEADING DEFENSE CONTRACTORS, 1959 *

Company	Number of Retired Military Officers Employed	Number of Retired Flag & General Officers Employed
Boeing	61	5
General Dynamics Corp.	186	27
General Electric	26	7
Lockheed	171	27
United Aircraft	24	5
American T & T	6	0
North American	92	8
Douglas	40	5
The Martin Co.	63	9
Hughes Aircraft	22	5

* Source: Subcommittee for Special Investigations, House Committee on
Armed Services, *Report*, 86th Cong., 1st sess. (Washington, D.C.: Government
Printing Office, 1960), p. 9.

raises serious doubts as to the complete objectivity of some of these
decisions." [7] This situation is a natural by-product of negotiated, as
opposed to advertised, contracting.

On the other hand, the employment of ex-military personnel can
of course help to foster a good working relationship with military
contracting officers once a contract has been secured. As distinct
from the perhaps unfair advantage gained in competing for contracts, this may be of benefit to military R & D in general. The
administration of research must be flexible because of the uncertainty and complexity of the work. Personal contact between
government and business administrators can serve to protect the
scientist or engineer from undue red tape and ease the completion
of assigned tasks.

The problem of placing checks on business power in lieu of the
market mechanism remains. Here Congress and the General Accounting Office, because of their independence from the Armed
Services-business relationship, have often proved to be more effective
than the contracting agency. The possibility of Congressional re-

[7] Subcommittee for Special Investigations, House Committee on Armed
Services, *Report*, 86th Cong., 1st sess. (Washington, D.C.: Government Printing
Office, 1960), p. 11.

crimination, coupled with the embarrassment of an unfavorable post-audit by the GAO, can at least check extreme abuse through simple fear of apprehension.

The imposition of administered price control in a nonmarket situation greatly reduces the common distinction between the public and the private spheres. Business firms are called upon both to exercise self-control and to keep subcontractors under close supervision. Equally striking, perhaps, is the fact that government calls upon firms to share in the implementation of broad policy goals that go well beyond the job at hand. Since small firms tend to be shunted aside in R & D work, Armed Services regulations require that enterprises holding prime or subcontracts encourage small business bids. Accordingly, large firms make a variety of efforts to inform small concerns of opportunities and to solicit submissions. To this end they work closely with government officials of the Small Business Administration and with the small business specialists of the Armed Services. Again, because defense contracts constitute a large monetary contribution to the economy (approximately $25 billion per year), prime and subcontractors are also called upon to pay due attention to labor surplus areas in the distribution of lower-tier contracts in order to help relieve unemployment in regions where it is acute. Military contractors must contribute to some of the more basic aims of public policy; the government, through its contracts, purchases not only weapons, but management and cooperation in the performance of public functions.

These changes in the orientation of government-business relations from frequent isolation and occasional antagonism to research alliance is vivid testimony to the profound effects that have resulted from the increased pace of scientific and technological progress. But the resulting research partnership between public and private institutions is complicated and delicate. While government and business may be allies of the scientific age, only government is strictly accountable to the public. Business, meanwhile, remains oriented toward its private interests. Congress and the GAO have frequently shown signs of concern at the extent to which private business is becoming involved in the making of public decisions. One instance of this concern has been the case of Space Technology

Laboratories, a wholly-owned subsidiary of the Thompson Ramo Wooldridge Corporation.

Through an Air Force contract, STL served as technical director of the ballistic missile program, and as such enjoyed a supervisory position over hundreds of firms. In order to ensure that STL not take unfair advantage of its position, the Air Force contract stipulated that it not participate in the manufacturing of components. Nevertheless, complaints arose that STL was making use of the knowledge derived from its Air Force assignment for private gain. The GAO recommended that the Air Force absorb the functions of STL, and the Air Force responded to the Congressional pressure that ensued by creating a non-profit institution, Aerospace Corporation, to take over the direction of the ballistic missiles program. The case of STL illustrates the possibilities of conflict of interest that exist in the present partnership between government and business. Despite the problems that are bound to arise in the partnership, however, the alliance of government and business must endure both because of the state of technology and because of the requirements of the Cold War.

Scientific Research and Military Needs

The urgent requirements of military security are almost wholly responsible for the staggering amount of government-sponsored research in business. The new weapons that have resulted have speeded changes in military technology on a scale hitherto undreamed of. Meanwhile, contemporary competition with the Soviet Union continues to demand the accelerating development of new weapons.

The Cold War has changed the basic nature of armaments races. The older armaments race, of which that between Britain and Germany before World War I is a classic example, was quantitative. The most important objective was to stockpile ever larger amounts of fairly standardized military equipment. By contrast, the present race with the Soviet Union is largely qualitative. Being heavily concerned with establishing leads in new weapons, it is really more an R & D race than a classic armaments race. Accordingly, the problem of coordinating scientific research for military need has assumed key importance.

One of the most difficult and important problems in coordinating the development of new weapons is what is commonly called "lead time." Lead time is the period between the conception of a weapon and its availability to the Armed Forces for use in the field. Experts and laymen alike have often chafed at the existing length of lead times. Among other things, they have blamed interservice pressure and rivalry. This rivalry has a civilian counterpart in contractor disputes and pressure from business for profitable production contracts. For instance, General James M. Gavin, former Army Chief of Research and Development, has pointed out that pressure from contractors has in some instances swayed the Armed Services to continue the production of weapons on the threshold of obsolescence.[8] In addition, much administrative time is taken up in negotiating contractual instruments, coordinating the work of contracting officers, assuring small business participation, and so on.

There have been two principal reactions to the problem of long lead time and the need for coordination. One of these, familiar to those who followed the post-Sputnik debates, holds that military R & D should be tightly centralized. The government should have a "science czar" or a "missile czar" to direct all military research and to abolish, or at least reduce, interservice rivalry. The second approach takes the quite different view that the government should foster more competition in R & D. Since the research process is uncertain by nature, the more duplication of effort, the greater the chances of reaching a solution in a short period of time.[9] While disparate, the approaches are not necessarily mutually exclusive.

The coordination of R & D for defense has been a continuing problem. During the War, the Office of Scientific Research and Development met with spectacular success. As part of the Executive Office of the President, OSRD had exercised powerful discretionary authority and had had the nation's outstanding scientific talent at

[8] James M. Gavin, *War and Peace in the Space Age* (New York: Harper & Brothers, 1958), pp. 255-57.

[9] For an extensive discussion, see Charles J. Hitch and Roland McKean, *The Economics of Defense in the Nuclear Age* (Cambridge, Mass.: Harvard University Press, 1960). Chap. 13.

its disposal. OSRD was successful not only in providing liaison among military research programs but also in recognizing and using multiple research approaches when appropriate. When OSRD was dissolved without a successor at the end of the War, the over-all responsibility for military R & D devolved upon the Department of Defense. A Joint Research and Development Board was formed and was shortly superseded by the similar, but somewhat more powerful, Research and Development Board.

Created in 1947, the Research and Development Board was patterned after the organization of the Joint Chiefs of Staff. It was composed of a civilian chairman and two representatives from each of the three branches of the Armed Forces. The work of the Board was performed by a six-member Executive Council, some fifteen technical committees, and numerous (over 100 in 1953) panels. The committees and panels, made up of part-time scientific advisers and representatives of the Armed Forces, were to obtain and analyze information about Armed Forces research programs and to recommend programs and policies for each of the Armed Services. The Research and Development Board itself

> was made responsible for preparing an integrated military research and development program. . . . It was directed to make recommendations on methods of keeping pace with scientific developments and on the assignment and coordination of research and development among the Armed Services; it was to advise the Joint Chiefs of Staff on research and development as related to military strategy. [In 1948] the Secretary of Defense authorized the Board to act for him on all research and development matters not involving major policy.[10]

In general, the Research and Development Board proved somewhat inadequate to its task. Since scientists were present only on a part-time basis, the military easily dominated the committees of the Board, and successfully resisted outside control of their own research appropriations. Efforts to allocate research programs among the Armed Services came into constant conflict with each Service's

[10] House Committee on Government Operations, *Thirty-Second Report— Research and Development*, 85th Cong., 2nd sess. (Washington, D.C.: Government Printing Office, 1958), pp. 62-63. Hereafter cited as House Gov. Ops., *Thirty-Second Report*.

idea of its general role and mission. Part-time scientific advisers had insufficient opportunity to think in terms of the broader policies needed beyond the areas of their own expertise. Unlike OSRD, the Board lacked authority to try out ideas of its own by financing research projects independently of the Armed Services. The former Deputy Chairman of the Research and Development Board, Don K. Price, concluded in epitaph that the Board,

> although it was the highest echelon in the scientific structure of the Department of Defense, did very little to lead the Department to take a unified look at the future of whole systems of weapons in relation to strategy. Instead, it tended to bog down in a detailed review of the specific scientific programs of the military departments and in efforts to prevent overlapping and duplication among them.[11]

The Research and Development Board was abolished in 1953. In that year, as a result of a report by an expert group headed by Nelson A. Rockefeller, a single officer entitled "Assistant Secretary of Defense for Research and Development" was made responsible for R & D in the Department of Defense. He inherited the duties previously vested in the Board. Then in 1956 DOD created a "Special Assistant to the Secretary of Defense for Guided Missiles" to supplement the work of the Assistant Secretary in that specialized field. In 1958 the Advanced Research Projects Agency was formed and authorized to carry out research projects with its own funds independent of any given branch of the Armed Services. ARPA may prove of considerable value; it restores to research coordinators the possibility of financing their own projects. This power was one of the strongest features of OSRD and its absence plagued the Research and Development Board. Also in 1958, the position of Assistant Secretary of Defense for R & D was abolished and replaced by that of Director of Defense Research and Engineering. The Director has broader powers than the old Assistant Secretary. In addition to the latter's coordination functions, he has direct authority over ARPA.

It is still too early to assess the value of the new centralization that the Director of Defense Research and Engineering represents.

[11] Don K. Price, *Government and Science* (New York: New York University Press, 1954), p. 147.

But the establishment of ARPA is significant. This agency enables the DOD to pursue research projects independent of the restrictions of any given branch of the Armed Services. As such, programs of longer-range military significance can receive backing without regard to shorter-run Service objectives.

ARPA is designed to placate the critics who hold that present military research does not allow for sufficient experiment along multiple lines of development. It complements the coordination function with a more pluralistic research effort. On occasion, the beneficial aspects of duplicating research efforts have been of proven value in reducing military lead times. In the case of the A-bomb, multiple research teams assigned to work on different approaches to the same question made possible the rapid solution of many critical problems. More recently, interservice rivalry itself proved valuable; Navy work on solid fuel missiles, for example, is now of great use to the Air Force missile program.

Much of the criticism of over-centralization in R & D has been focused upon the practice of tying R & D too closely to production, as is particularly the case in the weapons-system approach. A prime contract for a weapons system calls for the management and co-ordination of all phases of work, and is assigned immediately after a design competition. In place of this practice, the critics would carry competition among several firms through R & D to the prototype stage.[12] Production decisions would then be made on the basis of performance competition among prototypes, and the Armed Forces would be ensured the latest type of weapon that research competition might provide. This approach is undoubtedly sound from the strictly military standpoint of achieving maximum advance in weapon technology in the minimum time. But it is also more expensive, at least initially, than the present transition from a single prototype to production, and therefore involves the public policies that annually determine the level of R & D expenditure.

Budgeting for R & D

The question of whether government is spending "enough" on military R & D is closely related to the general debate on over-all

[12] See especially Burton H. Klein, "A Radical Proposal for Research and Development," *Fortune*, May, 1958.

defense and government spending. The level of government expenditure involves such high policy that it ultimately rests with the President and Congress. Within the context of all the competing demands for public money, there is no doubt that R & D has at least received considerable attention and there is every reason for believing that it will continue to do so. However, there are certain peculiar characteristics of R & D that warrant a discussion of a particular aspect of budgeting, that of budgetary cuts on an arbitrary basis. Unplanned expenditure curtailment for budgeting objectives has a highly adverse effect on military R & D. This problem was crystallized in 1957, when the administration imposed ceilings on military expenditure of funds already appropriated by Congress. As a result of the presidential order, the Secretary of Defense directed that a sum of about $170 million of R & D funds be transferred to production procurement, forcing the Navy and the Air Force to terminate over 300 R & D contracts. The deleterious consequences of this action were noted by a Congressional Report.

> In nearly every case there was extreme disappointment over the arbitrary and unheralded manner in which the cancellations were carried out. In most cases the projects had been initiated by the Government and many months of negotiation had taken place before the research teams were organized, contracts signed, and work gotten under way. Then, with work partially completed and without warning, a telegram arrived ordering the work to be halted immediately, "for the convenience of the Government." . . . Some of the major complaints of the contractors include the following: (a) Sudden termination notices are unplanned, unfair and do not provide for an orderly conclusion of the work. (b) Since the project is broken off before the crucial latter stages can be completed, there is little if any value to the Government. Oftentimes the costs of closing the contract are equal to what normal completion would have entailed. (c) There is a lowering of morale among all scientific personnel including those who remain in the laboratory as well as the ones laid off. (d) Research teams are broken up and the accomplishment of objectives delayed or defeated.[13]

Curtailment of R & D for purposes of budgetary expediency costs more than it is worth. Curtailed production can be stepped up again by reactivating equipment temporarily left idle, but

[13] House Gov. Ops., *Thirty-Second Report*, pp. 36-37.

R & D projects will be all but lost if not followed to completion. From the strictly military point of view, R & D curtailment can become a prime source of long lead times.

R & D expenditures deserve special budgetary treatment. R & D is a highly productive kind of government expenditure and lies at the heart of the defense effort. Its organization is a delicate matter, involving highly skilled manpower and complicated facilities. Under these circumstances, normal standards of government economy lose much of their relevance. Budgetary cuts based on short-term considerations can be positively inefficient when applied to R & D, and generally increased appropriations deserve close consideration.

Although the nation has greatly increased its research spending in money terms, inflated costs indicate that the increase in terms of manpower and facilities has been considerably less. A Naval study has estimated that the costs of R & D were inflated by 60 per cent in ten years, taking 1947-49 as the base years. Scientists' salaries led the cost components, rising 67.1 per cent over the base period. They were followed by indirect expenses (up 61.4 per cent), technicians' wages (49.5 per cent), equipment (49.5 per cent), and materials (31.5 per cent).[14] This cost inflation greatly reduces the significance of the postwar rise of R & D expenditure in dollar terms. Although the dollar level of military R & D obligations for 1958 was over three times that in 1950, correction for rising costs and accounting adjustments reduce the increase to something less than twice the 1950 appropriation level.

R & D and the Economy: The Patent Problem

How much the government should do to stimulate R & D ought not to be determined purely in relation to military need. In terms of its contribution to national prosperity, R & D is an indispensable tool in the promotion of economic growth. In the postwar years, military R & D has made substantial contributions to the civilian economy. Jet passenger aircraft and radar are just two of the spectacular innovations that have been made possible by government-financed research. Their adaption to the civilian economy, together with the employment and investment they have

[14] House Gov. Ops., *Thirty-Second Report*, p. 107.

generated, have been crucial to the performance of American industry.

The possibility of economic innovation is closely tied to the patenting of inventions. Patent policy, as was pointed out earlier, is as old as the Constitution of the United States itself. Patents constitute a traditional incentive for innovation; an American patent confers to the inventor monopoly rights over his invention for a period of seventeen years. The possibility of a temporary monopoly over a new good or process, or over the royalties to be derived from licensing an invention to other companies spurs business firms to make an invention before their competitors.

While the patent system has long proved useful in providing an incentive for industrial innovation, it deserves careful reexamination. Economically, the patent system suffers from two disadvantages. It does not guarantee that the inventor will make his invention available; he can choose to keep the invention off the market if this is to his advantage, thereby denying to the public the benefits of the latest technical knowledge. The patent system also causes wasteful duplication in R & D. If competing firms are unable to purchase a license authorizing the use of a patented invention, they may have to devote much effort merely to duplicate a patented invention by other means.

The economic disadvantages of the patent system are supplemented by administrative and judicial difficulties. Inadequately supported, the Patent Office has been chronically behind in its work. Congress is presently carrying out a far-reaching investigation of the patent system.

Clearly, there is a deep-seated need for revision, which some critics would carry as far as abolishing the patent system altogether. Professor Wassily W. Leontief of Harvard has recently pointed out that if speedy economic growth is desired, the free availability of the most recent technological advances to all comers would serve as a powerful stimulant. "[T]he economic benefits of scientific and industrial research can be exploited fully only if no one, no one at all, is prevented from using its results by the price which he has to pay to do so." [15]

[15] Wassily W. Leontief, "Introduction," Leonard S. Silk, *The Research Revolution* (New York: McGraw-Hill Book Co., Inc., 1960), p. 6.

As an alternative to the patent system, a viable policy might be to reward inventors with bounties paid directly by government. Likewise, governmental steps to encourage small business research might also be contemplated. The government could help establish cooperative research institutes to serve small firms, thereby restoring greater balance between big and little. It is generally acknowledged that smaller firms tend to be more aggressive innovators than larger ones.

Government can formulate new research policies that would act as strong stimulants to the broad pursuit of economic growth. The research establishment could contribute still more to the economy than it does at present if it were provided additional public support. So far, we have of course concentrated only on the purely industrial aspects of research. Perhaps even more important for growth in the long run are basic research and scientific manpower. In these areas, government comes into close contact, not with business firms, but with education.

3

UNIVERSITIES AND GOVERNMENT

World War II and its aftermath wrought a financial and organizational revolution in university research no less than in government and industry. In 1938, total funds spent on university research amounted to about $28 million.[1] Some of this money was provided by the universities themselves; philanthropic foundations constituted the only important source of outside funds. By contrast, 1958 research expenditure had mounted to $736 million, of which the federal government financed over two-thirds.[2] Only three years later the 1961 federal contribution alone was estimated at over $879 million.[3] This rapid influx of federal money can be attributed principally to growing recognition of the importance of research and to the rising cost of facilities and equipment. Presently, these funds are being supplemented by additional millions designed to stimulate the training of scientific manpower.

Government and University Research

The federal government has gone about financing university research in two principal ways. The government supports individual projects at universities through contracts and grants. It has also organized tax-financed research centers administered by the universities.

Research centers, set up through general administrative contracts

---

[1] President's Scientific Research Board, *Science and Public Policy*, I, 10.

[2] National Science Foundation, *Reviews of Data on Research and Development*, No. 19 (April 1960), p. 4.

[3] National Science Foundation, *Federal Funds for Science IX* (Washington, D.C.: Government Printing Office, 1960), p. 56.

between the government and the universities, are roughly similar to their industrial counterparts like the Sandia Corporation. Government agencies, usually the Atomic Energy Commission or the Armed Forces, provide the money and determine the broad objectives of the center. The universities supply business management and over-all technical direction. Government places its contracts for research centers either with a single university (the Los Alamos Laboratory is under the University of California at Berkeley) or with a group of universities (the Brookhaven National Laboratory is under Associated Universities Inc., which includes Harvard, M.I.T., and some ten other schools). In 1961, government spent about $390 million for university-managed centers. As a practical matter, research centers operate in a semiautonomous fashion. They are normally removed from the university campus and always employ their own research personnel.

While research centers have little relation to the internal affairs of a university, contracts and grants for individual projects profoundly affect all facets of university operations, from laboratories and budgets to faculty and students. Research projects are conducted within the universities themselves and form an integral part of the intellectual function of these institutions. Government support for such projects totaled $490 million in 1961 and constituted by far the largest source of funds.

When government finances university research, it often draws a distinction between *purchased* research (projects originating in the specific needs of government agencies) and *sponsored* research (projects proposed by university scientists for their general intellectual value). While this distinction can become somewhat tenuous, it has administrative implications for the method of support. The government frequently awards contracts when it wishes to purchase research, and grants when it sponsors projects. The latter carry fewer legal constraints and constitute specific recognition of the special nature of government-university relations.

Government-university relations are indeed quite different from those between government and business. Since business is oriented toward the (private) profit motive, the chief problem in government-business relations is to reconcile the performance of public functions with the profit motive. Universities, on the other hand, exist for the dissemination and accumulation of knowledge—more plainly, for the teaching and research that together make up higher education. With the growth of national concern for higher education, universities are becoming an important area of public policy. Meanwhile, the government performs an increasingly larger number of public functions, of which education is but one. Government-university relations bring together two publicly oriented sets of institutions, and hence the principal questions that arise concern conflicts between different public goals. To the extent that government support of research (or of manpower programs) comes close to the universities' ideal, it contributes to the public service of higher education. But to the extent that it forces universities to deviate from their goal, higher education will be sacrificed in favor of other public functions. To be sure, federal funds need not conflict with higher education even in the case of purchased research; specific agency needs often result in major contributions to knowledge. However, tensions between government and universities frequently arise over problems of finance and administration.

Loyalty-Security Requirements

A major area of administrative conflict has arisen from regulations regarding the loyalty of research personnel and providing for the secret classification of findings. These procedures ultimately affect all scientists, but have been of particular concern to the university as the home of free intellectual inquiry.

From one important perspective, loyalty-security requirements are ultimately a matter of benefits and costs. Whatever benefits they may contribute to national security must be balanced against important cost factors. Classification of information as secret can prevent or delay the publication of research findings, thereby impeding the free flow of ideas imperative for rapid scientific progress. Security checks and loyalty requirements will also involve some loss of scientific manpower in key areas (scientists of "questionable" loyalty), and can have a psychological effect that will keep even "loyal" talent out of necessary work.

Difficulties encountered in the loyalty-security program have led the government to reconsider its attitude on the question of loyalty as a qualification for federally-sponsored research not immediately related to military needs. In 1956 the executive ruled that henceforth "an allegation of disloyalty should not by itself be grounds for administrative action on a grant or contract for unclassified research by scientifically competent investigators." [4]

This reasonable stand has alleviated the problem posed by loyalty requirements, at least in research; but there remains the question of secrecy. Educational institutions universally dislike the presence of classified research on campus. Classified research not only impinges on the intellectual principle of freedom of inquiry but it also creates some extremely practical difficulties. The protection of secret work is a distinct nuisance to a university. Buildings or parts of a building may have to be sealed off from general use; precautionary measures ranging all the way from locked doors to alarm systems complete with guards can become necessary. For the researcher, classification can be positively harmful. If he needs access to pertinent classified information, he must still prove his "need to know" even if he has been cleared. Then, once he has completed his project, he will have to wait a lengthy period of time for declassification and publication, regardless of whether or not his findings turn out to be of concrete military value. In the case of younger scientists, classification can severely complicate the completion of the Ph.D., at times prohibiting possible thesis topics. These difficulties have led at least one major university, Harvard, to refuse all classified research. Nevertheless, approximately 10 to 15 per cent[5] of federally-supported university research remains classified, much of it in the field of nuclear physics.

Under pressure from the universities, the government has taken some steps to reduce on-campus secrecy. Many classified projects have been shunted off to research centers or industry. From time to time, necessity may dictate that a certain number of classified projects be performed on campus. In these instances, the government could do much to ease the administration of secrecy, which remains unnecessarily cumbersome. There is need for tighter standards, restricting classification to a smaller number of projects of distinctly military application. Also, much could be done to speed

---

[4] White House Press Release, April 4, 1956.
[5] National Science Foundation.

the workings of the administrative machinery of secrecy, so that projects will not remain classified long after the value of secrecy has been exhausted. If universities must continue to make sacrifices in recognition of government's need for secrecy, the government can do more to ease the burdens of classification. Revision of the classification process toward greater speed and efficiency would involve little cost; it is largely a matter of administrative procedure.

The Thorny Problem of Indirect Costs

While loyalty-security issues have received much public attention, some less well-known financial problems are perhaps even more important to government-university relations, notably those involved in federal reimbursement of the indirect costs of government-supported research projects.[6] Through their impact on the general university budget, federal policies on indirect costs affect for better or worse the over-all performance of universities. Government research projects, of course, cover all the direct costs involved (salaries of the principal investigator and his assistants, equipment, and other similar expenses), but there exists in addition a number of costs that cannot be allocated precisely to any given project. These include general administrative and accounting expenses, library services, maintenance of buildings and grounds, and the like. Such costs are called indirect costs, or overhead. Early federal support of university research paid only for direct costs; indirect costs were regarded as a university contribution to the advancement of knowledge generated by the research.

As federal support has grown, however, government contributions to overhead have increased. Beginning in 1947, the government, in what was known as the "Blue Book" formula, attempted to classify those elements of indirect costs toward which the Armed Services should make contributions. Meanwhile, the National Institutes of

[6] For excellent treatments of the indirect cost controversy, see House Committee on Government Operations, *Health Research and Training,* House Report No. 321, 87th Cong., 1st sess. (Washington, D.C.: Government Printing Office, 1961), pp. 60-70; Charles V. Kidd, *American Universities and Federal Research* (Cambridge, Mass.: Harvard University Press, 1959), chap. 5; James McCormack and Vincent A. Fulmer, "Federal Sponsorship of University Research," *The Federal Government and Higher Education,* The American Assembly (Englewood Cliffs, N.J.: Prentice-Hall, Inc., 1960), pp. 107-118.

Health gradually increased their overhead contribution to 15 per cent of direct costs. The National Science Foundation followed NIH procedure in making its own grants. Nevertheless, university complaints continued to mount in direct proportion to the annual increments in federally-supported research.

A principal source of dissatisfaction was the disparity between the NSF-NIH overhead allowances and those provided by the Armed Services and certain civilian agencies under the "Blue Book" formula. The startling extent of this discrepancy is illustrated in Table V, which summarizes the experience of eleven of the nation's leading universities with NIH grants during 1956-57. For these large-scale recipients, the smaller NIH reimbursement formula created serious budgetary drains; Harvard, for instance, suffered a loss of almost half a million dollars. This money had to come out of general university funds. The less generous overhead contributions made by NSF and NIH have been justified by the federal government on the basis of the distinction between "purchased" and "sponsored" research.

Table V

EFFECT OF NIH INDIRECT COST POLICIES
ON SELECTED UNIVERSITY BUDGETS, 1956-57 *

	Direct Costs Covered by NIH Grants	NIH Indirect Cost Allowance 15 Per Cent	Reimbursement Under Blue Book Formula	Deficiency Paid by University
Univ. of Chicago	$1,166,000	175,005	322,663	147,658
Columbia University	1,758,200	263,739	475,094	211,355
Harvard University	2,704,626	405,694	884,413	473,719
Indiana University	300,456	45,068	104,755	59,687
Univ. of Minnesota	1,113,852	167,078	341,270	174,192
New York University	1,171,711	175,757	420,401	244,644
Northwestern University	600,018	90,003	173,609	83,606
Ohio State University	210,276	31,541	59,479	27,938
Stanford University	868,322	130,248	272,219	141,971
Univ. of Washington	940,507	141,076	302,302	161,226
Univ. of Wisconsin	820,816	123,122	157,428	34,306

* Source: *Hearings—Statements of Members of Congress, Organizations and Interested Individuals,* Departments of Labor and Health, Education and Welfare Appropriations for 1959, Subcommittee of the House Committee on Appropriations, 85th Cong., 2nd sess. (Washington, D.C.: Government Printing Office, 1958), p. 32.

At the instigation of the universities, indirect cost policies have recently come under revision. Late in 1958, as a result of studies undertaken through the American Council on Education and the Bureau of the Budget, the "Blue Book" principles were somewhat revised in the direction of greater liberality. Among other provisions, the government allowed contributions to the cost of administrative salaries and increased the rate of reimbursement for library services. The revised principles, embodied in Circular A-21 of the Bureau of the Budget, represent an earnest attempt on the part of the government to meet all reasonable indirect costs. Circular A-21, however, like the old "Blue Book," applies neither to NSF or NIH, which presently account for about one-third of federal research contributions to universities.

In 1960, the National Science Foundation raised its overhead contribution from 15 per cent to 20 per cent of direct costs. However, because NIH remains tied to a 15 per cent level by its appropriation acts, the general problem remains acute. Medical research has emerged of late as the darling of Congress, which has made large annual increments in NIH appropriations, at times even going far beyond the recommendations of the Administration. The result naturally has been to increase indirect costs. The fact that most NIH funds flow into medical schools only worsens the situation. Universities have been forced to devote an increasing proportion of general funds to meet the overhead of medical faculties, leaving less money to devote to other departments.

The traditional views that have blocked full reimbursement of indirect costs are less understandable now than they may have been in an earlier context. At one time, "sponsored" research of projects proposed by the scientific community could justifiably have involved some sharing of costs with the universities. Congressmen are naturally prone to desire that money appropriated for research be stretched as far as possible for the direct support of individual projects. Scientists have frequently concurred in this view from a motive no worse than the normal selfishness inherent in any professional group. When federal research sponsorship was at a lower level, the universities could reasonably be expected to bear a part of the financial burden. As a proper university function, research has a claim on the university's general budget; federal grants aided the development of this function and were a source of institutional prestige. But drastic increases in government support are decisively changing the nature of the situation. Sheer financial necessity is quickly rendering obsolete the old distinction between "purchased" and "sponsored" research. And it is well to remember that this necessity is largely the result of a situation in which Congress now actually presses sponsorship on the universities.

While NSF and NIH have yet to succeed in coping fully with the problem of overhead reimbursement, they have recently turned to new means through which to alleviate the universities' financial plight. In July 1960, NSF announced an experimental program of institutional research grants. As distinct from the present grants that are strictly limited to individual projects, the new program will give universities unrestricted research money. In the words of the Foundation's official announcement, the grants "are intended to provide institutions with valuable flexibility for strengthening and balancing the particular activities to be undertaken with the funds. . . . [They] may be considered as interest paid to our schools on protracted loans made by them to the nation in the form of scientific research and scholarship." [7] The amount of each grant is to be five per cent of the total annual Foundation project grants made to the university in question, up to a limit of $50,000. NIH also initiated institutional grants in 1961, having received authority from Congress in September 1960. The formula determining the amount of the grants is roughly similar to that of NSF. The two programs represent an interesting innovation that should contribute to greater flexibility in university research, but it is worth noting that their amounts do not even make up the agencies' continuing deficits in indirect cost contributions.

Financing Capital Facilities

Our treatment thus far has covered only the problem of current or operating expenditure. But there is also the matter of capital facilities, ranging from standard laboratories to highly complicated and expensive equipment. Various agencies, particularly the Armed Services and the AEC, have installed such major facili-

[7] National Science Foundation Release, July 26, 1960.

ties as nuclear reactors for the use of university scientists. At times, these facilities have been set up as part of a research center managed under contract by one or more universities, as in the case of the Brookhaven National Laboratories. In other instances, facilities have been constructed as an integral part of a university campus through the provision of a specific project contract. Finally, a certain amount of government property has been made available to institutions under various Congressional acts regulating the disposal of surplus property.

It is only recently that the government has begun to finance research facilities as such without regard to specific contracts or research centers. In 1956 Congress passed a Health Research Facilities Act providing for the renovation and construction of facilities for research in the medical sciences. Under this Act, NIH has made grants totaling about $30 million per year. The grants are made to universities on a matching basis, requiring them to pay half the cost of approved projects. In 1960, the National Science Foundation, which has ordinarily provided grants for highly specialized facilities to answer individual needs, began a program of cost-sharing grants to universities for general purpose research laboratories.

In the years since Sputnik, considerable concern has been voiced within the scientific community and government over the age of existing facilities. Much of the present research capital dates from OSRD contracts of World War II, and many a laboratory building may even have roots in the nineteenth century. Contemporary science, meanwhile, often makes such rapid advances that facilities may be outstripped almost as rapidly as they are constructed. A recent report of the President's Science Advisory Committee underlines the question of facilities with a new sense of urgency.

> The dramatic expansion of science in this country has outrun our ability to provide up-to-date space and equipment. . . . While in the end men are more important than facilities, the immediate bottleneck today, in many fields and in many universities, is in buildings and equipment. . . . Very little good laboratory work can be done without a roof, and in experimental science the best equipment is usually the true economy.[8]

[8] President's Science Advisory Committee, *Scientific Progress, the Universities and the Federal Government* (Washington, D.C.: Government Printing Office, 1960), pp. 18-19.

Federal policy toward research facilities can bear considerable reexamination as the instance of cost allowances for the depreciation of university facilities well indicates. In typical cases, the government allows about 2 per cent of book value for the amortization of university-owned physical plant used in contract research. This means that the facilities in question are expected to remain serviceable for a fifty-year period. By contrast, business firms normally receive much higher allowances and have the initial advantage of tax write-offs. Higher rates for depreciation could enable universities to accumulate funds of their own for more frequent modernization.

The new matching grants now being made by NSF and NIH will also warrant close study. The cost-sharing provisions are designed to encourage private giving, but it remains to be seen whether private gifts will be forthcoming in amounts sufficient to help make up existing deficiencies. If they are insufficient, a bottleneck hindering adequate government aid will be created. In 1959, President Eisenhower recommended that the government meet the entire cost of constructing a $100,000,000 nuclear reactor at Stanford University to be used as a national facility for general research in the physical sciences. Congress has been studying the proposal and is expected to act favorably. This kind of spectacular project may well portend future large-scale financing of unrestricted research facilities.

Sputnik and the Manpower Muddle

In the past few years the financial problems of university research have received increasing attention from both the legislative and the executive branches of the government. Despite the importance of the issues involved, relatively little interest has filtered down to the level of general public discussion, partly because the issues are complex and difficult to reduce to readily understandable propositions.

In distinct contrast, scientific manpower has become a topic of extensive popular consideration, again largely because of Sputnik. The Soviet launching of the first manmade satellite in the fall of 1957 produced tension and a sense of failure throughout the United

States. In the climate of accusation and counteraccusation that immediately followed the event, the finger of blame was pointed at many facets of government and society. The administration was accused of pennypinching and lack of imagination; the Armed Services were scored for outdated strategic notions and childish wrangling over roles and missions; even the American scientist came in for his share of blame. Before long, however, national concern came to rest upon an area with only the remotest connection to the policy decisions that accounted for America's lag in the missile field: the educational system, and particularly science education.

Although public concern for scientific training is relatively recent, the government has helped to educate scientists for over twenty years. Leaving aside the Service Academies, ROTC programs, the G.I. Bill, and similar special stimulants to highly trained manpower, two principal contributors to general science training can be singled out: research assistantships connected with federal research contracts and grants, and graduate fellowships sponsored by NSF, NIH, AEC, and a few other agencies.

Ever since the large-scale introduction of federal research money to universities in World War II, assistantships have been a principal source of support to graduate students in the natural sciences. Almost all contracts and grants provide money for laboratory assistance to the principal investigator. Since the latter is a professor, he will normally appoint some of his graduate students to assistantships, through which they will contribute to his research and as a by-product accumulate research findings of their own that can even provide the core of a doctoral dissertation. The research assistantship clearly exemplifies the close connection between teaching and research.

The monetary compensation offered by research assistantships tends to vary from field to field and in accordance with the proportion of the student's time devoted to the work involved. Research assistants have normally been paid in the range of $1,500 to $2,000 per year. It is estimated that the value of research assistantships financed by federal grants and contracts presently lies in the vicinity of $40 million per year. Since this figure accounts for about one-fifth of all outside support received by graduate students, the importance of contracts and grants in scientific training is obvious, and tends to increase with every annual rise in research appropriations.

The research assistantship had been criticized as a far from ideal stimulant to graduate study and scientific careers. For one thing, although the work involved may frequently contribute to requirements for the Ph.D., it does not necessarily do so and may indeed lengthen the recipient's career as a student. More serious still is the charge that the availability of research assistantships channels the energy of students into work on fairly mundane problems and away from more imaginative dissertation projects for which support is not available. Many university departments also complain that research assistantships compete unfairly with teaching assistantships, reducing the manpower available for teaching large elementary courses.

Research assistantships are but a by-product of federal research sponsorship in the universities and are not considered a direct manpower program. Since the War, however, a number of agencies have initiated fellowship programs specifically designed to stimulate graduate study in the sciences. The largest current program, sponsored by NIH, provided some $60 million in 1960 for fellowships and training grants to encourage study of basic health science, public health, and related subjects. NSF, for its part, supports a now well-known graduate fellowship program, sponsors training for secondary school science teachers, and provides funds for lower-level science education. In 1960, NSF fellowships totalled $13 million and its remaining manpower programs $51 million. The AEC makes available over $10 million per year for various training and fellowship programs in the physical sciences. The government's greatly increased concern for manpower development since Sputnik can be gauged in part by the fact that NSF fellowship support has quadrupled since 1957, while NIH training appropriations have more than tripled.

Undoubtedly, however, America's principal monument to Sputnik is the National Defense Education Act. The Act represents the first peacetime effort to promote education on a general scale. Federal aid to education, of course, has been a continuing subject of debate since the War, and prior to Sputnik, a number of abortive attempts were made to secure Congressional approval of financial aid to schools and universities. Indeed, only ten weeks before Sputnik, a $1.5 billion school construction bill failed to pass the House of Representatives by a mere five votes. The National Defense Education Act was passed in the atmosphere of tension and confusion that was precipitated by the nation's suddenly conscience-stricken concern for its scientific posture. As such, it is a hodgepodge of provisions which are open to severe criticism, but which nevertheless represent some interesting new directions.

In essence, the National Defense Education Act provides $1 billion for a motley assortment of educational programs. The money is spread over the four-year period from 1958 to 1962. The Act, recently extended by Congress until 1964, provides both for direct subsidies to students and for various grants to educational institutions and states.

The student subsidy approach is twofold, combining a loan program for college and university students together with fellowship aid reserved for certain categories of graduate students. The loan program authorizes a total expenditure of $295 million which is allocated directly to educational institutions by state, according to the ratio that state enrollment divided by state population bears to the national enrollment divided by the national population. Colleges and universities are themselves responsible for the administration of the loans and must match every $9 of federal money with $1 of their own. Students may borrow up to $1,000 per year to a total limit of $5,000. The borrower must repay the principal within twelve years of graduation (exclusive of time spent in military service or further full-time study) and is charged interest at an annual rate of 3 per cent. Up to one-half of the loan can be forgiven if the borrower enters the teaching profession.

The NDEA authorizes 5,500 fellowships for graduate study with stipends ranging from $2,000 for the first year to $2,400 for the third and subsequent year, plus an additional $400 for each dependent that a student may have. Most significantly, the Act provides for direct payment to universities of additional sums up to $2,500 for each of the fellowship recipients enrolled. Thus, an attempt is made to help universities meet those costs over and above tuition that are incurred through the admission of federally-subsidized students. Like the loan program, the National Defense Fellowships reveal a desire to increase the supply of teachers. The Act stipulates that preference be given to applicants interested in teaching in institutions of higher education. Unlike the loans, however, fellowships are awarded directly through the Commissioner of Education and not through the universities concerned. Undoubtedly the most important stipulation in the fellowship legislation is that students be enrolled in a "new program [of graduate study] or an existing program which has been expanded." The intent of this stipulation is plainly to strengthen those smaller graduate institutions that, unlike the large established universities, do not already cover the complete range of graduate study. The Act states specifically that an important objective of the National Defense Fellowships is that of "increasing the facilities available in the Nation for the graduate training of college or university level teachers and of promoting a wider geographical distribution of such facilities throughout the Nation."

In addition to the student subsidies just described, the legislation provides for a welter of programs to stimulate educational facilities at all levels of schooling and in numerous branches of study. Leading the list in financial terms is an allocation of $296 million for equipment to be used by public schools in science, mathematics, and language courses. The money is given to state governments under the guise of grants-in-aid that require the states to supply matching funds. The amount of the grant paid to any individual state is determined in part by the state's school-age population and in part by the relation between state income per child of school age and national income per child of school age. The effect of the latter is to provide a relatively higher portion of federal money for the poorer states which, because of their low fiscal capacity, find it difficult to provide school facilities at a level that characterizes the wealthier parts of the nation.

The next two largest programs also require contribution from state governments and involve $75 million to improve the guidance and counselling of public school students and $60 million for vocational education. The funds authorized for guidance and counselling are intended to improve means of testing and advising students in order to channel them into the pursuits best suited to their ability, and to identify outstanding students and encourage them "to complete their secondary school education, take the necessary courses for admission to institutions of higher education, and enter such institutions." The appropriations authorized for vocational education are designed to help pay for a wide variety of expenses, from teachers' salaries to equipment purchases, entailed in providing vocational education opportunities to residents of areas now served inadequately. The intent of Congress is partially "to meet national defense requirements for personnel equipped to render skilled assistance in fields particularly affected by scientific and technological developments."

The National Defense Education Act has met with considerable criticism. Possibly the most controversial and best publicized part of the Act has been a clause that was inserted into the statute at a fairly late stage in the legislative committee process and passed almost unobserved by Congress. This is a clause that requires applicants for National Defense Education Loans and Fellowships to sign a loyalty oath together with an affidavit of disbelief. When the Office of Education undertook to enforce the provisions of the Act, the affidavit of disbelief evoked sharp criticism. By executing the affidavit, the student swears "that he does not believe in, and is not a member of and does not support any organization that believes in or teaches, the overthrow of the United States Government by force or violence or by any legal or unconstitutional methods."

What is perhaps at first glance a relatively innocuous statement does indeed raise some very serious questions. First, the reference to simple "belief" without any standard of evidence is extraordinarily vague. Second, the term "organization" is open to virtually any interpretation. Congress gives no indication of what specific organizations it has in mind, even as to whether or not these are on the standard Attorney General's list. Third, by placing the burden of loan administration on the universities themselves, the Act forces these institutions into the uncomfortable position of inquiring into their own students' fundamental beliefs and freedom of association. Finally, because NDEA loans require matching funds from the universities, the latter find that some of their financial aid funds become tied up by outside restrictions.

The affidavit controversy represents the latest chapter in the seemingly endemic conflict of academic freedom and federal control. Protracted negotiation was necessary before the federal government finally yielded on loyalty restrictions for nonmilitary research grants. Student fellowships granted by the National Science Foundation do require a loyalty oath and affidavit, but these are administered strictly by NSF and are required of recipients only. The National Defense Education Act, in requiring oath and affidavit even from mere applicants, carries loyalty procedures considerably beyond prevailing federal practice and forces the universities themselves to participate both financially and administratively in the application of the restrictions.

Statements denouncing the affidavit of disbelief have come from all quarters, including liberal organizations, the American Association of University Professors, numerous universities, and many Congressmen. A small number of universities, including certain Ivy League schools and others of similar prestige, actually turned down NDEA funds and have refused to participate in the program. This was a difficult decision, for these universities, in weighing principle against material welfare, had to forego additional loan funds and hence force sacrifices on their needier students. While some highly influential Congressmen, including the present President of the United States, have exerted serious efforts to persuade Congress to repeal the affidavit, they have met with no success, in part because of willful committee delays, in part because of reluctance to drag Congress into an open fight that might divert it from more pressing issues. Their principal hope now rests on the possibility of securing a technical amendment in prospective revisions of the legislation.

Although the loyalty provisions of the National Defense Education Act have provoked serious controversy and forced some painful decisions, they should by no means be regarded as the only shortcoming of the Act. To proponents of federal aid to education, the Act is only a piecemeal measure, a foot in the door. It has no provisions for badly needed school construction or teachers' salaries. Nor does it provide general scholarships and fellowships to university students, although a provision for these came close to being adopted. In an educational sense, the Act is likewise open to serious question. It seems to place heavy emphasis on engineering, technical vocations, and similar "practical" subjects. In its emphasis on guidance and "teacher training," it draws the wrath of those who oppose the pedagogical philosophy of the teachers colleges and "educationists," of those who call instead for a return to substantive training in the academic disciplines. As a matter of general criticism, one caustic opponent offered the following as an extreme caricature of the Act:

> The "educated man" envisioned by the bill will be an engineer, spotted as talented early in life and carefully guided into his useful profession. He will have been taught by television, and may have picked up a bit of conversational Bengali. After graduate school he will owe the federal government something like a year's pay. In order to borrow it, he will have taken a loyalty oath five times and signed five loyalty affidavits (one basic vaccination and four booster shots each). To pay the money back he will probably go to work in a defense plant.[9]

While overly harsh, this caricature does reflect the compromise nature of the Act. Indeed, the NDEA, both by what it does and does not provide, offers piecemeal satisfaction to various groups without wholly satisfying any of them. The loans and fellowships answer demands for student aid; the fellowships in particular support the pleas of the lesser universities. Grants for science and language facilities appeal particularly to hard-pressed school boards and educational administrators. Teacher training and guidance provisions are in part the province of teachers colleges and educationists, while the vocational education funds placate another strong and specific interest group. The loyalty oath and affidavit constitute a bow in the direction of hyper-loyal Americans, and finally the absence of general scholarships, provisions for academic salaries, and school construction grants placate those inclined toward fiscal conservatism and states' rights. The Act attempts to be all things to all men and its shortcomings are excused under the guise of an emergency based on defense requirements.

Here again we can discern the continuing thread that runs through the relationship between the federal government and educational institutions: the nation's defense position in the Cold

[9] Daniel P. Moynihan, "A Second Look at the School Panic," *The Reporter* (June 11, 1959), p. 14.

War. Congress legislates not for education *qua* education but rather for education in relation to real or imagined defense needs. But defense requirements that may appear from time to time in the course of the Cold War need not necessarily coincide with long-run educational objectives. The many weaknesses of the National Defense Education Act are inherent in the second word of its title.

Whatever the shortcomings of the Act, however, no critic can deny that its programs are having an appreciable impact on American education. During 1960, 1,357 participating institutions of higher education distributed loan money to 115,450 students. The National Defense Fellowships have been awarded to 2,500 students spread among 139 graduate schools. The large number of graduate schools is significant, as is the fact that the fellowships are widely spread among fields of study. Of total fellowships awarded in 1960, approximately 57 per cent were in the humanities and social sciences, 36 per cent in the natural sciences and engineering, and 8 per cent in education. The high proportion of fellowships in non-scientific fields would seem to indicate that the NDEA is redressing in part an over-all pattern of federal support that has perhaps been disproportionately weighted in the direction of the sciences. In the area of science, mathematics, and language facilities for schools, the Act made possible 47,976 different projects in fiscal 1960. During the same year it helped to finance 46 language and area centers, 42 teacher-training institutes and 598 vocational education programs. If nothing else, the NDEA underlines the almost insatiable need of the American educational system for additional funds.[10]

Higher Education and Government Policy

What is to come during the present decade in the further development of federal relations to education is a matter for the broadest conjecture. Some indication may be gleaned from the projects that Congress had under consideration in 1961. From the welter of bills and amendments that were offered, two clear-cut sets of proposals emerged, both of which received strong backing from the Kennedy administration made explicit in a Presidential message

[10] All data in this paragraph are drawn from Department of Health, Education and Welfare, *Report on the National Defense Education Act, Fiscal Year Ending June 30, 1960* (Washington, D.C.: Government Printing Office, 1961).

to Congress on February 20, 1961. The first was a bill seeking to enact the School Assistance Act of 1961.[11] This most recent step in the continuing attempt to secure broad federal assistance to education concentrated on general school construction and teachers' salaries. For these purposes, the bill would have made available $2.3 billion to the states in the form of grants-in-aid. These grants did not require matching by state funds and varied from state to state in accordance with each state's level of personal income per public school pupil, thereby yielding proportionally more federal money to the poorer states. The second set of proposals was embodied in a bill entitled the College Academic Facilities and Scholarship Act.[12] The bill provided for loans to colleges and universities totalling $300 million annually in each of the five years from 1961 through 1965. These loans would have enabled the borrowing academic institutions to undertake the construction of a wide range of facilities including classrooms, laboratories, and libraries. The bill also sought to authorize the expenditure of approximately $150 million over the same five-year period for general scholarships carrying stipends of up to $1,000 and open to all college students.

While Congress rejected both bills, the plain fact is that the federal government is under ever increasing pressure to become further involved with the educational system. To be sure, there exist a number of important complicating factors in educational legislation, including such thorny questions as aid to racially segregated schools and colleges, grants or loans to private and denominational institutions, the constitutionally sanctioned responsibility of the states for education and the relative independence of all educational institutions from overriding federal control. These are all justifiably bound to be the subject of continuing debate, and will undoubtedly play a considerable role in shaping various programs. But the undeniable fact remains that American education is in a state of acute fiscal need, and that federal funds will inevitably be forthcoming.

The implications of growing federal concern for education are bound to have a broad impact on universities with their twin functions of teaching and research. Some aspects of the revolution

[11] 87th Cong., 1st sess., S. 1021.
[12] 87th Cong., 1st sess., H.R. 5266.

in federal-university relations in the field of research have already been touched upon. Meanwhile, growing concern for educated manpower bears heavily on the teaching side of the university equation. In terms of their total effect on universities the various segments of federal education policy cannot be rigorously compartmentalized. School aid programs, by increasing and ameliorating physical facilities, and by stimulating and improving the teaching profession, raise the quality of elementary and secondary education, and very probably increase the number of students aspiring to college study. Loans, undergraduate scholarships, and graduate fellowships, by bringing higher education within the financial reach of growing numbers of students, will add to the presently heavy demands being made on university facilities and faculty. Finally, federal demands for research give every sign of continuing their upward trend, as national concern for military security, better health, and scientific prestige continue unabated. In the light of these pressures, the universities themselves are not only becoming more closely tied to the government, but indeed can be considered as agents of national policy. Just as the national need for applied research, weapons, and innovation has softened the traditional distinction between government and business, so have the universities entered the arena of public policy not only as recipients of grants and performers of basic research but as full-fledged partners.

In view of these trends, there is a need for careful formulation of federal policy in favor of higher education. While American universities have always claimed financial need, present federal programs for research and the stimulation of skilled manpower will actually increase their burden. University demands on such relatively minor matters as full compensation for the indirect costs of research and faster rates of amortization for facilities used in federally-supported work deserve the closest consideration. Government policies in regard to student subsidies and loans, and grants for general facilities also require careful evaluation. Since the bulk of student aid is expended on tuition, much of the money is bound to find its way into university treasuries. But in all the major institutions of higher learning, tuition payments represent only a portion of the cost of a student's education. The remaining cost is made up by endowment, state appropriations, and the like. As federal aid to manpower increases, the universities may find that they are becoming unable to sustain their level of contribution to educational costs. They will then be forced either to raise tuition hastily or to seek additional government subsidy on a crash basis. By working together, the universities and the government should attempt to forestall such harmful improvisation through a realistic appraisal of educational costs. In this regard, the provisions of the National Defense Education Fellowships which entail direct federal payments to the university for each fellowship recipient deserve consideration. Through this method, the government helps the universities to meet the costs that arise from the attendance of federally-supported students.

On the subject of facilities, some serious questions arise regarding the relative use of loans and grants. A number of scientific agencies have recently initiated or increased various facilities grants, and general legislation for loans is now pending before Congress. Loans, of course, constitute one means of meeting existing physical needs, but they must be repaid in the long run. Since most university facilities, with the exception of dormitories, are not readily self-liquidating, loans might place educational institutions in highly embarrassing positions in the long run. Also, the universities' ability to repay them would tie in closely with levels of tuition, endowment, and state appropriations, which are presently being strained to meet operational costs that show every sign of increasing.

The area of federal-university relations has always been delicate, and promises to become more complex. In a scientific age, research needs and manpower requirements are tying education and government together with ever-tightening bonds. Further expenditure of money is inevitable but will not constitute a panacea; academic independence is bound to be a serious issue, at it has been in the case of the loyalty provisions of the National Defense Education Act. Just as the universities must pay close attention to the achievement of governmental aims, so must the government give due consideration to the special problems and goals of its intellectual partner. The scientific age, in cementing the nation's governmental and educational institutions, is bound to raise difficult problems of accommodation on both sides, as it has in the area of government and business.

4

FORMULATING SCIENCE POLICY

Historically, the role of science in the federal government has steadily expanded along four broad fronts. From the time of Jefferson's Patent Office, the first public function of science in America has been that of furnishing various technical services for national development and welfare. Since the Civil War, science has been linked increasingly to national defense until, in the 1960's, it takes the form of a sprawling network of organization for military research and development. After World War II, pure science began to receive close government support as the value of basic research achieved national recognition. Most recently, government has displayed growing concern for the development and training of skilled scientific manpower. As the relation of science to government has developed along these broad fronts, so also have the public and private spheres become linked in a partnership directed toward meeting the acute technological needs of an economically advanced society.

The increasingly technical character of important policy decisions has created a corresponding need for scientific advice in the policy councils of America. Scientific work has also played a fundamental role in altering the traditional separateness of the federal government, business, and the universities. In this context, a number of policy questions have assumed unprecedented importance. How should the nation coordinate the scientific research efforts of multifarious government agencies, business firms, and educational institutions? How should the government allocate its funds among pure research, applied research and engineering development, and among military, health, and agricultural research? What should be done about new scientists and new directions in research, about developing science for domestic and international purposes? What portion of the national budget should the government devote to the general scientific establishment as opposed to other important responsibilities such as military personnel and procurement, social security, agricultural price supports, urban renewal, and all the other competing demands for public money?

These and other broad questions can ultimately devolve only on the nation's highest policy-making organs, the presidency and Congress. Since elected officials require expert advice, however, the place of science at the top of the policy pyramid has become a matter for much concern and debate.

Science and the Presidency

Government machinery offering the possibility of general scientific advice dates from the creation of the National Academy of Sciences during the Civil War. However, with the exception of brief flurries of activity during World War I and the Depression, science did not really take a place in the councils of the presidency until World War II. At that time, through the Office of Scientific Research and Development under Vannevar Bush, science was firmly ensconced in the Executive Office of the President. OSRD was dissolved in the general demobilization that followed victory, but since 1946 a general trend has gradually operated to return science to the White House. With the demise of OSRD, important questions affecting military R & D passed from immediate proximity to the President down to the Research and Development Board at the Department of Defense level. Where the presidency was concerned, only the Bureau of the Budget remained as an executive arm for the coordination of research, and this only in a rather limited fiscal sense.

The Steelman Report of 1947, *Science and Public Policy,* made two principal recommendations to fill the gap in executive scientific advice. The first suggested that the President create an Interdepartmental Committee on Scientific Research and Development composed of "those bureau chiefs or other officials of the Government most deeply concerned with scientific research and development." [1] According to Steelman, such a Committee

> would provide a means of bringing to bear on major problems the scientific advice and counsel already available within the federal research establishments. The Committee's collective judgment would carry weight on a variety of vital subjects—formulation of integrated policies on science by the Government, the broad balance among the scientific undertakings of the Government, and the adequacy of administrative policies, such as for personnel. . . . The Committee would be much better able than any one department or agency to maintain a broad view of the nation's interests. [2]

The Steelman Report's second recommendation was that the President appoint a member of the White House Staff to serve as his scientific liaison officer and hold the post of executive secretary to the Interdepartmental Committee.

President Truman created the proposed Interdepartmental Committee in late 1947, but he did not follow through by appointing a White House science adviser. At this time, the debate over the creation of the National Science Foundation was in full swing. As outlined in Vannevar Bush's *Science, The Endless Frontier*, one of the Foundation's more important functions would be to "develop and promote a national policy for scientific research and scientific education." [3] After the protracted legislative struggle over the mode of its organization, NSF emerged in 1950 with general policy formulation as one of its functions. In addition, it was requested "to evaluate scientific research undertaken by federal agencies." [4] It thus appeared that NSF might assume the task of coordinating scientific research and the role of a science adviser to the President. But after a few vain attempts by the executive to make the agency an effective organ of coordination, NSF renounced any coordinating powers in 1957. As nothing more or less than one of many executive agencies, NSF does not hold a position in the governmental

---

[1] The President's Scientific Research Board, *Science and Public Policy*, Vol. III, p. 23.

[2] *Ibid.*, p. 24.

[3] Vannevar Bush, *Science, The Endless Frontier*, p. 28.

[4] *The First Annual Report of the National Science Foundation* (Washington, D.C.: Government Printing Office, 1951), p. 2.

hierarchy that would enable it to oversee other departments and agencies and offer top-level policy advice.

During the period preceding Sputnik, the Interdepartmental Committee thus remained as the executive's principal arm of coordination. But while the Committee was able to perform a number of useful tasks, especially in compiling inventories of federally-owned scientific equipment and facilities, it suffered from the relatively low administrative position of its members. They were not men of policy rank, such as assistant secretaries or agency heads, but were rather administrators approximately at the bureau chief level. The Interdepartmental Committee was perhaps further limited because its membership was restricted to government officials, leaving out representatives of the remainder of the nation's scientific establishment.

In an attempt to secure outside advisers at a relatively high policy level, President Truman created a Science Advisory Committee in 1951 and attached it to the Office of Defense Mobilization. After a six-year absence, science had returned to the Executive Office of the President, but with only indirect access to the Chief Executive through the Director of ODM. While the Science Advisory Committee was made up exclusively of part-time members, it did benefit from their eminence. Such names as James Bryant Conant, Lee DuBridge, and J. Robert Oppenheimer appeared on its first roster. The Science Advisory Committee gradually achieved increasing importance, especially under the Eisenhower administration. Then the ascent of Sputnik suddenly occasioned a rapid promotion for science in the policy hierarchy.

In a nationally telecast address on November 7, 1957, President Eisenhower announced that he had created the post of Special Assistant for Science and Technology, and tapped James R. Killian of M.I.T. as the first incumbent. At the same time, he promoted the Science Advisory Committee from ODM into direct contact with the presidency. The Special Assistant has received an extremely broad mandate and in effect serves as the President's personal adviser on all policies having a scientific bearing. As such, he has access to Cabinet and National Security Council proceedings, he can inquire into all government programs that bear on science, and he can communicate his advice and recommendations to the President on a person-to-person basis. He draws closely on the work of the President's Science Advisory Committee (PSAC), and in effect provides the liaison between that body and the President. Under prevailing practices, the Special Assistant serves as Chairman of PSAC, which is composed of seventeen nongovernment scientists who sit as full members, together with a number of government administrators, such as the Director of the National Science Foundation and the Defense Department Director of Research and Engineering, who sit in as consultants.

Very soon after their establishment, the Special Assistant and PSAC suggested the creation of a third administrative device to aid in the formulation of national science policy—a Federal Council for Science and Technology. The Council, created by Executive Order on March 17, 1959, is composed of the Special Assistant for Science and Technology; a representative of policy rank from each of the Departments of Defense, the Interior, Agriculture, Commerce, and Health, Education and Welfare; the Administrator of the National Aeronautics and Space Administration; and a Commissioner of the Atomic Energy Commission. Representatives of the Secretary of State and of the Director of the Bureau of the Budget may attend meetings of the Council as observers. Thus composed of high level government personnel, the Council is to consider problems of science and technology that cut across the missions of federal agencies, and is to make recommendations on the general administration of federal scientific programs. While not officially designated as such, the Special Assistant serves as Chairman of the Council. The Council replaces the old Interdepartmental Committee on Scientific Research and Development, whose lower level members continue to serve the Council as a standing committee.

As presently constituted, then, the new science policy machinery in the executive provides the President with expert scientific advice through PSAC, and with the means of coordinating scientific activity through the Council. The Special Assistant serves as kingpin of the structure by virtue of his twin chairmanships of PSAC and the Council and his personal access to the President himself. Science is thus incorporated into the inner sanctum of presidential decision-making.

Congress and Executive Reorganization: Proposals for a Department of Service

As the executive apparatus for national science policy was being built up, the legislative branch of government agitated on its own. It is largely from Congress, more specifically from the Subcommittee on Reorganization of the Senate Committee on Government Operations, that a movement arose for a Cabinet-level Department of Science and Technology. While a small number of influential individuals toyed with the idea of a Department of Science, it can appropriately be considered the brainchild of Senator Hubert Humphrey of Minnesota.

In the pristine form that it assumed in the wake of Sputnik, the notion of a Department of Science envisaged an organ that would include roughly all the scientific research branches of the various government agencies. After refinement in Committee, a concrete proposal emerged for a Cabinet-level Department that would have included the following:[5] (1) the three executive agencies not presently tied to existing departments, i.e., the Atomic Energy Commission, the National Aeronautics and Space Administration, and the National Science Foundation; (2) the basic research activities presently carried out in the Department of Defense; (3) a number of the science-oriented subdivisions of the Department of Commerce, including the National Bureau of Standards, the Office of Technical Services, and the Patent Office; and (4) all the operating functions of the Smithsonian Institution, "except those relating to the operation of museums . . . and of the Washington Zoo." [6] The Department would thus house those large agencies that are almost entirely oriented toward science and a number of organizations whose services are not closely linked to the primary missions of the departments in which they are presently housed.

Proponents of a Department of Science on this scale have mustered a number of arguments to support their cause. The Secretary of such a Department, through his Cabinet rank, would assure

[5] Senate Committee on Government Operations, *Science and Technology Act of 1958*, Document No. 90, 85th Cong., 2d sess., 1958 (Washington, D.C.: Government Printing Office, 1958), pp. 2-41.

[6] *Ibid.*, p. 10.

greater national status for scientific activity. He would assume a unique position of leadership in the political pursuit of scientific interests. The Department itself would curtail needless duplication and achieve a more rational allocation of scarce scientific skills. It would also provide a focus of clear-cut responsibility for the programs under its wing. Finally, it would constitute a policy link between Congress and the President that is presently denied by the centralization of scientific advice in the White House. In the words of Senator Humphrey, the Special Assistant and PSAC tend "to preempt the scientists who are thoroughly informed and conversant about governmental science operation for the benefit of the President alone, and effectively prevent . . . the Congress from obtaining information from qualified experts in the fields of science." [7]

Reasonable as the above arguments may appear on initial examination, opposition to a Department of Science was quick to materialize along a massive front. The 1958 session of the Parliament of Science, sponsored by the American Association for the Advancement of Science, roundly denounced the idea of such a Department, thereby bringing the organized voice of the broad scientific community into opposition. Numerous scientists personally testified against the creation of a Department in Congressional Hearings, and finally the executive branch, reflecting the opinion of the scientists through the President's Special Assistant for Science and Technology and the National Science Foundation, voiced emphatic disapproval and helped to stall the legislative proposal in committee. In general, the substantive basis for opposition to a Department stemmed from the scientists' distaste for centralization and from a number of sound administrative and political principles.

On close analysis, the proposal for a Department of Science is indeed open to question. The basic problem raised by the proposal is that government science remains overwhelmingly the province of mission-oriented departments such as Defense, Agriculture, and Health, Education and Welfare. Since these departments must retain their own scientific establishments, a Department of Science would embrace only a part of government science. Since it would be

[7] Hubert H. Humphrey, "The Need for a Department of Science," *Annals of the American Academy of Political and Social Science,* Vol. 327 (January 1960), p. 34.

within the Cabinet, such a department would be forced to assume the role of a competitor rather than a general coordinator. As Don K. Price has lucidly pointed out:

> A conventional step toward agency prestige in Washington is to get status as an executive department, which . . . carries "cabinet rank," or the right to be present in the President's cabinet meetings. But the price paid for this prestige is that a department must get its powers and its funds by legislation, and its head must be confirmed by vote of the Senate; thus the prestige that comes from direct power must be fought for in the political arena. This battle always involves rivalries among departments as well as between parties. Few things in politics seem more obvious than the probability that almost every executive department would join, together with its political friends in Congress, in attacking any proposal to pull its scientific research agencies out and transfer them to a central Department of Science. The secretary of such a department, in order to exist, would be committed to constant political warfare. In such a situation, he would be quite unable to serve as a close and confidential adviser to the President.[8]

To include in a Department of Science the three major scientific agencies that are not presently attached to executive departments, namely, the AEC, NASA, and NSF, raises still other problems. All three were created by Congress as independent agencies precisely in order to highlight their individual roles and missions. Two of these agencies, AEC and NASA, have at least as much status and political importance as most cabinet departments. Their inclusion might well give rise to internecine strife within the Department, with resulting pressures that would seriously limit the Secretary's effectiveness. Finally, inasmuch as both AEC and NASA are oriented toward practical missions, NSF might run the risk of seeing its basic research programs shunted aside. As the NSF strongly contended in protesting the creation of a Department,

> past experience has shown that often "applied research drives out basic," that is, that owing to the competition for funds within an agency which has both research interests and operating programs, applied research which contributes directly toward success of the

[8] Don K. Price, "Organization of Science Here and Abroad," *Science*, Vol. 129 (March 20, 1959), p. 762. Reprinted from *Science* by permission.

operating programs tends to be emphasized at the expense of the
more remote, less certain findings of basic research.[9]

As the dispute over the feasibility of a Department of Science
unfolded, Lloyd V. Berkner, the President of Associated Universities, Inc., offered an organizational compromise whereby the projected Department would include only those smaller scientific
agencies not intimately associated with the missions of the departments in which they presently find themselves.[10] Berkner's Department would thus include such agencies as the Weather Bureau, the
National Bureau of Standards, the Coast and Geodetic Survey, the
Hydrographic Office, the Fish and Wildlife Service, and the Naval
Observatory. These agencies, in Berkner's words, "have no real
organic relation to the departments with which they are indi-
vidually associated, but find themselves assigned to one department
or another largely through historical accident." [11] Berkner's proposal
has its merits; it would attempt to give important, but relatively
neglected, areas of science a place in the Washington sun. But it
carries a corresponding disadvantage inasmuch as the projected
Department, being necessarily small, would be too weak to afford its
components any protection from the tempests of interdepartmental
strife. The established departments in which the service agencies
presently find themselves can offer certain advantages because of
their long-standing relations with Congress.

Somewhat akin to Berkner's suggestion is that made by Dr. Wallace R. Brode for a limited Department of Science that would
emphasize the basic research aspects of scientific functions presently performed within the several departments and agencies.[12]
But Brode's Department offers little more prospect of political
strength, and would probably receive even less support from the
scientific community since the Parliament of Science of the AAAS,

[9] National Science Foundation, *9th Annual Report, 1959* (Washington, D.C.:
Government Printing Office, 1960), p. 11.

[10] Lloyd V. Berkner, "Government Sponsorship of Scientific Research," *Science,*
Vol. 129 (March 27, 1959), pp. 817-821.

[11] *Ibid.,* p. 820. Reprinted from *Science* by permission.

[12] *Create a Department of Science and Technology,* Hearings on S. 676 and
S. 586, Part I, 86th Cong., 1st sess. (Washington, D.C.: Government Printing
Office, 1959), pp. 70-84

in rejecting the idea of any cabinet department, stressed the argument that "to set up a department of science for basic research alone is undesirable since it would segregate exactly those parts of science least relevant to political issues and place them under the direction of a cabinet officer who is automatically and properly a political appointee." [13]

Plainly, the idea of a Department of Science has both its pro's and con's, although the latter appear to have the balance strongly in their favor. For the present, a Department of Science finds virtually no support, be it among politicians, administrators, or scientists. While certain proposed advantages or disadvantages of a Department may continue to be the subject of debate, there is no doubt that cabinet status for science does not offer a satisfactory substitute for policy formation within the White House proper. In a very real sense, science is now too important for mere cabinet representation. Like economics, it pervades all the key aspects of government policy and defies organization within a neat executive pigeon-hole. Just as the President is served by a Council of Economic Advisers within his Executive Office, so must he have readily at hand the counsel of professional scientists that the Special Assistant and the Science Advisory Committee can provide.

Some Continuing Questions of Policy Organization

The serious weaknesses endemic in the proposals for a Department of Science should not dismiss all thoughts of change in the structure of the federal scientific establishment. That the creation of a Department of Science should have become an important issue indicates the feeling among many responsible individuals that the present mode of organization leaves room for improvement. Attention is called to two points in particular: the question of Congressional liaison and the further strengthening of the President's advisory bodies.

Congress has had a fluctuating record in its concern for government science. As subsequent chapters show, only a few years have

[13] "1958 Parliament of Science," *Science*, Vol. 127 (April 18, 1958), p. 855. Reprinted from *Science* by permission.

elapsed since Congress and science were barely on speaking terms. But ever since Sputnik, Congress has shown not only growing concern, but relatively enlightened interest in the expansion and application of scientific research, particularly as it relates to such national goals as defense and health. In the organizational sense, Congressional committees naturally parallel the mission-oriented executive departments with which they deal. Thus such committees as Agriculture, Armed Services, and Labor and Public Welfare cover legislation that includes those science policies relevant to the appropriate executive agencies. Since 1946, however, Congress has had a Joint Committee on Atomic Energy which deals specifically with the affairs of the AEC, and, as an aftermath of Sputnik, two new committees were created with a still more specific attachment to science, namely, the Senate Committee on Aeronautical and Space Sciences and the House Committee on Science and Astronautics. As its name implies, the latter Committee has a relatively broad mandate in the field of science, and its jurisdiction includes NASA, the National Bureau of Standards, and the National Science Foundation.

Such distinguished spokesmen as Senator Humphrey who continue to stress the need for closer scientific liaison with Congress have a number of organizational alternatives open to them. For example, Congress could broaden the scope of the Senate Committee on Aeronautical and Space Sciences and the House Committee on Science and Astronautics to the point where each of the two chambers would have a committee covering all aspects of government research and development. This proposal would enable selected Congressmen to acquire an over-all view of the science establishment and would give scientists a common forum for their public testimony. But it would also be bound to give rise to jurisdictional conflicts with the established committees already charged with overseeing the policies of the mission-oriented departments, and might be a source of needless duplication. A joint committee on science including members of both House and Senate would be subject to exactly the same virtues and defects.

A final possibility would be the creation of a committee similar in scope to the Joint Committee on the Economic Report. The latter, having no legislative responsibilities, serves a purely informative, educational, and advisory function. It concentrates its attention on the President's annual economic report, takes testimony from businessmen, government officials, and private economists, and has sponsored a number of important studies dealing with fundamental economic problems. A committee for science modeled on the Joint Committee on the Economic Report might well provide science with the middle ground between the presently fractured committee process and a centralized committee on science legislation burdened by questions of jurisdictional conflict. Coupled with an annual report issued by the President through his Special Assistant for Science and Technology, such a committee would provide a closer relationship between the executive and legislative branches than presently exists in the making of science policy, and might stimulate appreciably greater interest in scientific matters both in Congress and in the nation as a whole.

Of course, it is possible to argue that science cannot achieve the same proximate relationship to Congress as economics; that Congressmen can never become as concerned with science as with economic policies that directly affect the pocketbooks of their constituents. But Congress shows signs of developing ever greater appreciation of science as it relates to economic welfare and national security. The continuing efforts of the Joint Committee on Atomic Energy, the excellent studies on various aspects of space sponsored by the House Committee on Science and Astronautics, and the current investigation of the patent system by the Senate Subcommittee on Patents, Trademarks and Copyrights are all indicative of growing Congressional concern for national policies with a scientific content.

While the subject of scientific liaison with Congress is receiving due attention, the new science advisory machinery in the White House is being subjected to continuing examination. A period of three or four years gives relatively little basis on which to evaluate the performance of the Special Assistant, the President's Science Advisory Committee, and the Federal Council for Science and Technology, but these organs have generally met with approval. After a recent study, however, the Subcommittee on National Policy

Machinery of the Senate Committee on Government Operations, chaired by Senator Henry M. Jackson, has made certain criticisms and suggestions.[14]

According to the Subcommittee, the Special Assistant and PSAC have not entirely fulfilled their mission of planning, developing, and encouraging new fields of scientific advance. In making this charge, the Subcommittee places the blame largely on the fact that the science advisers have a relatively small staff. It also points out that while the members of PSAC have spent large amounts of time on the job, their part-time capacity narrows the President's immediate accessibility to scientific information. Where coordination of science programs is concerned, the Subcommittee criticizes the Federal Council for Science and Technology in much the same terms as its predecessor, the Interdepartmental Committee:

> The Federal Council, as an instrument for assisting the President in monitoring agency programs, has been of only limited utility. It has worked under the limitations of all inter-agency coordinating committees of its kind. Where programs stakes are high, and agency differences deep, departmental heads have traditionally tried to by-pass Council-type mechanisms. The balance of bureaucratic power is weighted heavily against the Federal Council.[15]

The Jackson Subcommittee would remedy the above difficulties by grouping the Special Assistant, PSAC, and the Federal Council in an Office of Science and Technology within the White House. The Office of Science and Technology would be set up by statute (which the present advisers are not), giving it a more stable underpinning. As Director of the Office, the Special Assistant would be given two full-time deputies, chosen from PSAC for periods of one or two years, and would employ a larger number of staff assistants than at present. Finally, since the Office would be specifically charged with the task of giving technical counsel to the Bureau of the Budget, it would help provide for closer coordination of science programs.

[14] Subcommittee on National Policy Machinery, Senate Committee on Government Operations, *Organizing for National Security: Science Organization and the President's Office*, 87th Cong., 1st sess. (Washington, D.C.: Government Printing Office, 1961).

[15] *Ibid.*, pp. 4-5.

The relatively limited recommendations of the Jackson Sub-committee have a strong element of caution. In a way, they provide little change over the present organization beyond an enlargement of staff that will almost certainly be needed as the tasks of the Special Assistant expand. How far the recommendations would go toward meeting the criticisms of the Subcommittee is another question, but the work of the Subcommittee indicates a continuing attempt to improve the nation's machinery for science policy formulation. Present questions involving science are so important and complex that the government should undoubtedly keep its modes of science organization under constant surveillance. In this regard, Dael Wolfle has wisely written that "An organizational change may sometimes be justified not because the new pattern is inherently better than the old one but because the change provides an opportunity to bring in new blood and to accomplish the reinvigoration that in an ideal world would not be necessary." [16]

Science offers a particularly crucial and difficult challenge to government organization. It has an advisory aspect, whereby policy makers require highly technical counsel in the making of decisions; it is also involved in substantive programs, through which billions are spent for its development and consequent contributions to national objectives. If welfare and security are to be promoted with vigor, the nation's scientific establishment promises to be an ever more serious charge. The size and cost of the establishment mean not only that the government must assume a leading role, but that the partnership which has been created between public and private institutions must be maintained and strengthened. Cementing this partnership will require imagination, courage, and a degree of accommodation on all sides. This is the very stuff of national politics, involving not only the top echelons of elected and administrative officials, but the scientists who will be counted upon to advise them.

[16] Dael Wolfle, "Government Organization of Science," *Science,* Vol. 131 (May 13, 1960), p. 1415. Reprinted from *Science* by permission.

PART TWO

POLITICS

5

ARMS AND THE SCIENTIST

On the level of public policy, science and the nation come together, as we have seen, at many points, including health, education, and the economy, as well as defense. In political terms, however—which is to say, in the effort to shape policy—scientists have been most active in those matters touching the military application of their work, and only sporadically active in other areas. Contributions of modern research have made it conceivable that some ever impending total war might annihilate civilized life itself. More immediately, the products of science weigh heavily in the international balance of power. Scientists everywhere have therefore developed a special concern with what comes of their work. In the United States this concern has been most evident among the "atomic scientists," many of whom have played active and important parts in recent political history. They have discussed problems and formulated policies among themselves and with scientists of other nations. They have on occasion made themselves lobbyists for legislation in the area of their interests. They have also, as scientific advisers, participated in the making and unmaking of military and foreign policy.

The role of scientists in the politics of national security should not be exaggerated. Immediately after World War II it was sometimes imagined that scientists were about to become Homeric demigods who would lock arms to decide the fate of their nations. Even recently a scientist has contended that "if a world war should ever break out again, it will be a desperate slugging match between the scientists and engineers of the contending nations, with the rest of the population as unhappy bystanders." [1] In the last decade, however, we have experienced a number of "limited" wars in which soldiers, not scientists, continue to play the most active part. It remains true that scientific and technological factors are only among the elements of military preparedness—which is itself only one component of foreign policy. Many groups with technical skills are essential to the formation and implementation of foreign policy. In numerous instances, moreover, other affiliations and influences have affected the political inclinations of scientists as much as their professional role.

Nevertheless, it remains true that scientists have become a new and a peculiarly unsettling element in the process by which certain of our political decisions are made. That process has long been unsettled by the tendency, at work in all advanced industrial societies, toward the concentration of effective authority in the hands of elected and appointed officials. Experts provide advice not easily questioned by laymen, and they are often charged with the implementation of necessarily broad social goals. Before acting on decisions affecting national security, frequently secret, political representatives need not seek public approval. Their only inhibition, not always effective, is their accountability for the results. Specific criticism of foreign policy is frequently blunted by overriding concern for national unity.

Where democratic participation and explicit consent are thus in effect ruled out, political indifference, bureaucratic inertia, and defensive self-interest may be expected to converge in a steady but dangerously unimaginative course. If government is to display initiative and responsibility, surrogates for active democracy become essential. One such surrogate is the interplay of the corporate interest of departments, agencies and bureaus. Still another is the exercise of professional responsibility, especially on the highest levels of government, by those whose ability and training have put them at or near the helm. Like it or not, we have no choice but to depend upon them to provide the governmental process with foresight and independence of judgment; to consider other than narrow department or group interests; to present, and to select from, alternatives

---

[1] Arthur R. von Hippel, "Answers to Sputnik," *Bulletin of the Atomic Scientists* (hereafter cited as *BAS*), Vol. XIV, No. 3 (March 1958), p. 117.

reflecting our national aspirations. Like other skill groups enmeshed in government—and often to a greater degree—scientists find themselves faced with the new opportunities, the challenges, and the risks of professional responsibility.

No surrogates will ever satisfy those who believe in democracy, but as the only alternatives to bureaucratic inertia and popular apathy and ignorance, these have real attractions. The experience of the scientists in politics is therefore an engaging set of lessons in the nature and problems of professional responsibility and at the same time in the adjustments demanded of self-governing societies that would remain viable and strong in the modern world.

Scientists and Warfare in the Past

J. B. S. Haldane relates that according to legend a renowned medieval commander, the Chevalier Bayard, was so determined to keep the art of war within courtly bounds that in dealing with captives who had made use of gunpowder he refused to honor the chivalric code.[2] Nevertheless, it is safe to conjecture that technological progress has always been stimulated by the desire for more effective instruments of predation and protection. Usually in the past, however, technical developments originally conceived for other purposes have been found also useful in battle. In recorded history military innovations most frequently come as by-products of scientific work, often unintended or unanticipated. The compass and the steam engine both had enormous consequences for naval warfare, but neither was deliberately conceived for such purposes. The invention of the telegraph and radio greatly expanded the scope and coordination of all military operations, but neither Morse nor Marconi, nor the others whose contributions made their inventions possible, would have considered their work military research. This is equally true of Thomas Edison and of those who developed the internal combustion engine, the automobile, the early airplanes, and balloons.

Among occasional exceptions to the typical pattern, James Boyle offered his services to the British Army on the basis of his study of

[2] J. B. S. Haldane, *Callinicus, A Defence of Chemical Warfare* (London: K. Paul, Trench, Trubner & Co., Ltd, 1925), pp. 28-29.

ballistic trajectories; Vauban, the great French civil engineer, dedi-
cated his considerable talents to developing fortifications for the
armies of Louis XIV; Da Vinci produced the premature design for
a submarine intended to enable the Florentine republic to achieve
naval advantage over commercial rivals (though he suppressed it
for fear of its military usefulness); and even Galileo was no stranger
to the Venetian arsenal, which provides the setting for his *Dialogue
of the Two World Systems,* though it does not seem that he made
any specific and direct contributions to the art of war.

In American history, the various branches of the military grew
only gradually to appreciate and to encourage scientific research.
They were content either to sponsor general investigations, such as
those supported by the Naval Observatory, or to improve known
weapons. Not until the Second World War did the U.S. Army and
Navy establish programs of scientific research that were not headed
by officers "who knew what was needed in combat" and that were
designed not to supply known requirements but to provide altogether new weapons.[3] The experience of the cavalry, which for
years held out against the machine gun, was not completely lost on
the strategists.[4] In general, however, the rate of advance was
sufficiently slow and unspectacular to allow a gradual adaption of
armory, tactics, and ethic without mortally endangering armies
which resisted too proudly.

The invention of dynamite in 1866 marks what is probably the
first momentous step toward the modern relation of scientific discovery to warfare. In retrospect, Alfred Nobel's legacy establishing
prizes for scientific achievement and for contributions to world
peace might seem a symbolic recognition that scientific advances
made war more to be dreaded and avoided than ever. Actually,
Nobel himself believed that universal possession of so frightfully
destructive a weapon would in itself cause war to be avoided or
even eliminated as an instrument of international competition.
Statesmen, he reasoned, would now be far more prone to settle their
differences peacefully than to resort to battle. In the light of sub-

---

[3] Don K. Price, *Government and Science,* p. 58.
[4] See Edward A. Katzenbach, Jr., "The Horse Cavalry in the Twentieth
Century: A Study on Policy Response," *Public Policy,* Vol. VIII (1958), pp.
120-150.

sequent history Nobel's gesture appears, by the most charitable estimate, a utopian prelude to the assertion of political responsibility by scientists.

Not until World War I did scientists play so important a role in warfare that they could begin to envision themselves as rivals to the professional soldier. In purely military terms the most significant innovations of the War were probably those that greatly increased mobility on land and through the air—the tank, the weapons carrier, the balloon, and the airplane. But even though it claimed far fewer casualties and has since been discarded as a weapon, it was poison gas, more than any other development, that brought to light the changing relation of scientists to warfare.

A poisonous gas, chlorine, was first employed in the War by the Germans at Ypres in April, 1915, an event which provoked the Allies to make frantic efforts to develop protective devices and gases of their own. One of the most instructive and provocative commentaries on gas warfare in World War I is the lecture delivered in 1924 by J. B. S. Haldane, the chemist. In defense of chemical warfare, Haldane argued that the use of poison gas had been decried only because it was new and scientific. It was no more immoral than bayonets, shells, and incendiary bombs. In fact gassing resulted in a far lower proportion of fatalities to total casualties than the other methods of warfare. The effects of the weapon had been made to seem more horrible than they were by propaganda, such as inspired a widely known painting showing a column of blinded soldiers groping their way back from the front single file, each with an arm on the man ahead. The blindness induced by mustard gas, Haldane noted, was almost always temporary. Gases that produced only temporary paralysis and disorder might even be considered humane weapons.

The professional soldiers, Haldane contended, opposed gas warfare, not on moral grounds, but because such a coldly rational way of killing contradicted the notion of war as a gentlemanly sport. They were reluctant to accept these unromantic weapons and even more reluctant to take the advice of the scientists who produced them. The Germans, he suggests, might well have won the War had they been prepared to take full advantage of their priority with the new weapon. But they refused to take seriously the estimates of their scientists and did not have reserves in readiness to push through the gap opened in the lines when gas was first used. (Anti-Semitism, according to Haldane, was also costly because it prevented the Germans from seeking the services of their best physiologist to develop an effective respirator.) Nor were the British much more receptive. To appreciate the attitude of some scientists toward the professional soldier, consider one of Haldane's comments on the "military mind":

> How profound and unreasoning the objection of the military mind to chemical warfare is can best be judged by one simple fact. About three years ago the British regular army gave up the instruction of every soldier in defence against hostile gas. For one thing, speed in adjusting respirators being of more importance than elegance, it did not form the basis of a satisfactory drill, like those curious relics of eighteenth-century musketry which still occupy so much of the time of our recruits. But the truth no doubt was that the officers did not like that sort of thing. The chemical and physiological ideas which underlie gas warfare require a certain effort to understand, and they do not arise in the study of a sport, as is the case with those underlying shooting and motor transport. One of the first acts of the late Labour Government was to reinstate some modicum of anti-gas instruction in the normal training of the Army. But it may be hoped that this pernicious and demoralizing teaching will once more be dropped with the return to power of one of the gentlemen's parties.[5]

After the War other scientists, lacking Haldane's enlightened cynicism, vented similar antagonism to militarism by dramatizing the horrors of gas warfare and demanding that it be banned from use. Notable among those who took this position was the Cambridge Scientists' Anti-War Group in England. In any case, after reviewing the evidence of the War and later developments, military planners concluded that gas would not be a very effective weapon in a foreseeable future war. It was probably at least as much because of this military judgment as for reasons of officer-class psychology that the drill was abandoned.

Gas attack was at least contemplated in World War II. The German High Command is reported to have seriously considered using gas when the Russians counterattacked and when the western

<hr>

[5] J. B. S. Haldane, *Callinicus*, p. 35.

Allies invaded Normandy, but is believed to have desisted from fear of reprisal. On Iwo Jima the U.S. considered using gas to flush Japanese defenders from caves and other redoubts. The retired chief of the Army Chemical Corps testified after the War that because the U.S. refused to employ gas, the conquest of the Island cost 25,000 American casualties, including 7,000 dead, to defeat 21,000 Japanese, who were killed with the far more horrible white phosphorous and flame throwers.

In 1939 German chemists came upon the "nerve gases," since adopted by other powers, which are both lethal and difficult to detect. Both the U.S. and U.S.S.R. are known to have developed nerve gases for possible military use. But the most recent additions to the arsenal of chemical weapons, and perhaps the ones with the most revolutionary military significance, are the so-called "psychochemicals" that produce temporary paralysis and induce hallucinations and reversal of behavior. When fully developed these new chemicals may be capable of so disabling a defending force as to permit an enemy to capture it intact without opposition and without casualties to either side.

Like chemistry, but on a much smaller scale, biology was also found to have military application during the First World War. German agents are said to have secretly infected horses shipped from the U.S. to Europe. In World War II a special Japanese detachment was alleged to have used biological warfare against personnel in China. Here also modern developments portend more significant military applications than have yet been experienced in actual warfare.[6]

The major significance of gas warfare, however, is that as a demonstration of the value of science to the military arsenal it foreshadowed later developments. If Haldane could indict the military for an irrational resistance to the innovations of chemistry, he was

[6] See House Committee on Science and Astronautics, *Research in CBR* (*Chemical, Biological and Radiological Warfare*), 86th Cong., 1st sess. (Washington, D.C.: Government Printing Office, 1959); *Chemical, Biological and Radiological Warfare Agents, Hearings before the House Committee on Science and Astronautics*, 86th Cong., 1st sess. (Washington, D.C.: Government Printing Office, 1959); and Subcommittee on Disarmament, Senate Committee on Foreign Relations, *Chemical-Biological-Radiological (CBR) Warfare and Its Disarmament Aspects*, 86th Cong., 2nd sess. (Washington, D.C.: Government Printing Office, 1960).

not so much the rational scientist that he could look with equanimity upon even more dangerous innovations that his colleagues in physics would one day produce. "Of course," he noted in 1924, "if we could utilize the forces which we now know to exist inside an atom, we should have such capacities for destruction that I do not know of any agency other than divine intervention which could save humanity from complete and peremptory annihilation." Fortunately, he felt, such a development was quite unlikely. "We cannot make apparatus small enough to disintegrate or fuse atomic nuclei," he wrote with prophetic assurance, "any more than we can make it large enough to reach the moon." [7]

Between the Wars: "The Beautiful Years"

For the physicists particularly, but also for scientists generally, the interwar years were "the beautiful years," as Robert Jungk has described them.[8] The community of science drew upon the warmth and vitality of masters, disciples, and colleagues in learning and life, held together not alone by considerations of mutual benefit but by a profound commitment to science. For some, this commitment was ultimate and primary, as for Max Weber when he spoke of the pursuit of knowledge—"science" in the broadest sense—as a "vocation" affording a personal freedom through consciousness in a world in which other values seemed arbitrary and illusory. For others, science still held the promise of social emancipation and fulfillment summed up for the Enlightenment by Condorcet in his description of the progress of knowledge as the force destined to create whole societies of men both educated and free. Still others, like Veblen, laced Enlightenment hope with technology, assigning a larger role to engineers and industrialists. There were those, too, for whom science was not an ultimate or exclusive pursuit but one among many which in no way contradicted a religious ethic or political conservatism. Science could be an expression of profound wonder at the universe or an outlet for curiosity. From all these perspectives emerged two common characteristics: a spirit of dis-

[7] J. B. S. Haldane, *Callinicus*, pp. 15, 17.

[8] Robert Jungk, *Brighter than a Thousand Suns, A Personal History of the Atomic Scientists* (New York: Harcourt, Brace & Co., 1958), pp. 10-47.

covery and a spirit of fellowship. The first promoted a competition for knowledge, the second kept that competition from degenerating into a petty scramble for eminence and priority.

This golden age was shaken and then overthrown by the intrusion of politics, first through the rise of ideologies which did not respect the autonomy of science. In Bolshevik Russia, Lenin denounced the physics of Ernst Mach because his theories seemed to contradict the "laws" of dialectical materialism. Stalin later made genetics a concern of the party "line" by lending official support to the work of Trofim Lysenko against the much more widely accepted doctrines linked by Lysenko and his followers with the names of Mendel, Morgan, and Weismann. Stalin seems to have been motivated by several interests in this most celebrated instance of political control over Soviet science. Ideologically, the assertion of Lysenko that acquired characteristics were inherited seemed to support the Marxian emphasis on the plasticity of nature and the effectiveness of environmental reform. Economically, the Lysenko theories seemed to encourage the prospect for an improved agricultural yield desperately needed to appease discontent and provide capital for industrialization. Culturally, the Lysenko camp drew upon an indigenous Russian school of thought whereas other geneticists belonged to alien schools of thought. Politically, Lysenko benefited from the support of workers' groups in agriculture (against the academic geneticists) and of the Central Committee of the Party.[9]

Less spectacular but more comprehensive than the Lysenko controversy was the effort of the Soviet regime under Stalin to make all Russian science politically reliable. So keen was the need for trained specialists that at first the Party was ready to overlook ideological nonconformity. By 1927, however, political examinations in Marxism were required of advanced students in the natural sciences, and in 1929 a thousand loyal Communists were ordered enrolled in the higher schools of science. Teachers were dismissed and tried in secret, and "practical" or "productive" subjects were stressed over theoretical studies, which had been the stronghold of

[9] The discussion of Soviet science in this and the following paragraphs benefits from the excellent article by David Joravsky, "Soviet Scientists and the Great Break," *Daedalus* (Summer 1960), pp. 562-581. See also his *Soviet Marxism and Natural Science: 1917-1932* (New York: Columbia University Press, 1961).

the older scientific intelligentsia. Where Russian scientists made significant progress, despite these efforts at political control, it was only because they left philosophy to the non-scientists, emphasizing the practical consequences of their work, and because the regime itself early recognized the industrial and military value of science.

In Nazi Germany, Hitler's ideologists repudiated the belief in universal science and universal humanity, so profoundly integrated by Goethe and Kant. Instead they put forth the bogus notion of "German science," a typically Nazi mish-mash of nationalism, racism, and elitism brought into play not only to purge "non-Aryan" personnel from the universities and laboratories but even to deny the validity of their work—most notably, of Einstein's theory of relativity. It took some daring in 1937 for even so eminent a physicist as Werner Heisenberg to publish in a leading Nazi newspaper, *Das Schwarze Korps,* a defense of Einstein's theory. Subjected to violent attack, Heisenberg sought the protection of Heinrich Himmler, head of the S.S. After investigating Heisenberg's loyalty, Himmler offered to grant him protection with the implicit understanding that Heisenberg meet the Nazis half way. In a letter acknowledging Heisenberg's loyalty, Himmler added a tactful postscript: "P.S. I consider it best, however, if in the future you make a distinction for your audience between the results of scientific research and the personal and political attitude of the scientists involved." [10] This sensible distinction, from the Nazi point of view, between Einstein and his theory, did not settle the matter. In 1940 Nazi physicists discussed their differences with other physicists convinced of the validity of relativity theory and solemnly agreed to sign a protocol accepting the theory of relativity. In 1942 a similar agreement was negotiated stipulating that "Aryan" scientists had created the foundations of the theory that Einstein merely pulled together with no original contribution of his own.

The Nazification of German science was the severest blow to the old community of scientists. All at once it severed the bonds of friendship and enterprise, separating scientists into opposing political camps. Worst of all, from the point of view of those scientists, most of them forced into exile, who stood opposed to the Nazis,

[10] The story is told in Samuel A. Goudsmit, *Alsos, the Story of a Mission* (New York: H. Schuman, 1947), p. 118.

was the fact that their own former colleagues had accepted and implemented the dictates of the "New Order." Those remaining German scientists who argued against Nazi interference with science, did so not in defense of the old community but on the grounds that to expel scientists and deny valid theories could only weaken German science. Perhaps, under the circumstances, this argument was the only one calculated to serve the interests of the old community with any effectiveness. It has been argued in defense of the German scientists that by staying at their posts, they kept the direct control of science out of Nazi hands. No doubt they were also moved to acquiescence, as were other responsible elements in Germany, in the hope that Hitler's electric appeal for a national awakening would have beneficial results while the early excesses of Hitlerism would soon disappear. Even on its best face, however, this position remains a far cry from that sense of international fellowship and the commitment to universal truth which had flourished together in Germany before Hitler.

The Atomic Scientists and the Bomb

It was of course none other than the "non-Aryan" refugees of Nazism, and in one or two instances "nonproletarian" refugees of Soviet Communism, who set in motion and sustained a merger of government and science the like of which had scarcely been imagined. The record of these events is now familiar. In 1939 Leo Szilard, a refugee from Hungary, and Enrico Fermi, a refugee from Italy, persuaded George Pegram, an American physicist at Columbia University, to make the first approach. Pegram wrote to the Navy Department broaching the information that it might be possible to obtain energy through inducing atomic fission and that this energy might be used in a weapon of tremendous destructive power. Pegram's appraisal of the scientific possibilities was still so doubtful that the Navy merely asked to be kept informed of developments. The Naval Research Laboratory had already sought to encourage atomic research and a visit from Fermi intensified interest. But in the absence of interest at a higher level, no very concrete support was forthcoming. The situation changed radically only after Szilard and Fermi, joined by two other refugee physicists, Eugene

Wigner and Edward Teller, persuaded the most celebrated of the new Americans, Albert Einstein, to write the now famous letter to President Roosevelt which opened the way to government support for atomic research.

Not without hesitation and reflection did these particular scientists, and others for whom they were in effect spokesmen, make the political commitment such a request presupposed. Recognizing before nonscientists the possibility of exploiting atomic energy for military purposes, they had to consider that German scientists might learn how to control atomic energy first and provide Hitler with a perhaps decisive weapon. They could no longer rely on the solidarity of the scientific community to forestall such a calamity. Moreover, as reluctant as they were to provide politicians and generals with weapons of such unprecedented power, they felt that to do otherwise, by deliberate abstention or default, was to advance the infinitely worse prospect of continued Nazi conquest. Nor were the refugee scientists the only ones to make such a firm political commitment. In 1939 Professor Percy Bridgman decided to close the doors of his Harvard laboratory to students from nations under dictatorial rule. American scientists began to impose a voluntary censorship on their publications concerning atomic energy. At the defeat of France in 1940 the Curies made certain to send their precious liters of heavy water off to England.

These instances of a new political commitment followed upon the poignant last act of the old community. In 1938 Otto Hahn and Fritz Strassmann in the Kaiser Wilhelm Institute in Berlin, stimulated by the news of unexpected results in an experiment of Madame Joliot-Curie in Paris, conducted experiments which proved to be the first laboratory demonstration of the splitting of uranium into two other elements. Hahn quickly sent the news to his exiled colleague, Lise Meitner, then in Stockholm. Miss Meitner discussed it with her nephew, O. R. Frisch, and together they wrote and submitted to the British periodical *Nature* an explanation of the results of the experiment. Frisch meanwhile hastened to inform his teacher Niels Bohr in Copenhagen of what had happened. Together they discussed the possibilities that seemed to be open for obtaining atomic energy. Bohr brought the news to the United

States shortly thereafter and the refugee physicists followed. In this whirlwind of international communion and discovery, the old community became a memory and a new era of political commitment came into being.

Government and Atomic Research

Although shrouded in deep secrecy before and during the War, the steps through which atomic energy was developed under government auspices are now well known. Responding to the scientists' appeal, President Roosevelt appointed an Advisory Committee on Uranium headed by Lyman W. Briggs, director of the National Bureau of Standards. Briggs and the other members, representatives of the Army Ordnance Corps and the Navy Bureau of Ordnance, met with the scientists and approved an initial contract of $6,000 to support experimentation for a year at Columbia University along the lines they suggested. (Eventually the cost of the first atomic bomb was to be put somewhere in the reaches of two billion dollars.) Scientists at other universities, notably Chicago, California (Berkeley), Princeton, and Harvard, joined in the efforts.

The most immediate and dramatic result came from the group at Chicago headed by Fermi, which produced the first controlled chain reaction in history in a "pile" of hand-hewn graphite blocks in which were embedded chunks of commercial uranium. This was an important step in convincing scientists, the government, and industry of the importance of the research, but in itself it was not enough to induce a radically larger government involvement. While Fermi's experiment and the discovery of the element plutonium in Ernest Lawrence's Berkeley laboratory moved independent scientists to urge more extensive support, much of the credit, direct and indirect, for putting atomic research under higher priority belongs to the political exploitation of research developments in America and England by Vannevar Bush and James B. Conant, aided by other leading scientists and by the National Academy of Sciences.

While American researchers were finding that plutonium seemed to have suitable properties, word came from Britain that the committee studying the prospects for an atomic explosive had decided that a bomb using U-235 might conceivably be developed in time for use in the war. The British committee, named Maud (for no particular reason), had therefore recommended that the government push the project forward with all possible speed.

Armed with news of both developments, Bush and Conant pressed for more vigorous action. After asking Arthur Compton to conduct an appraisal of the program for the President by a committee of the NAS, Bush conferred with Roosevelt and Vice President Henry Wallace in October and secured a commitment of large-scale support.

The report of Compton's NAS Committee, submitted in November, considered it more likely than did the Briggs Committee that atomic research might have militarily beneficial results soon enough to affect the conduct of the War. The Committee recommended increased support and, after consultation with engineers, also proposed that the government establish a central laboratory. Informed of these recommendations, President Roosevelt asked the Academy Committee and the Briggs Committee on December 6, 1941, to form a new "S-1 Committee" which would have at its disposal several million dollars from the President's special discretionary fund. The S-1 Committee was to operate under the NDRC, now within the new Office of Scientific Research and Development. By June, 1942, work had advanced so rapidly that it was considered time for the Army to join the enterprise. Under the Corps of Engineers a project was established under the code name, "Development of Substitute Materials." In September, 1942, Brigadier General Leslie R. Groves was appointed director of the DSM project. Afterwards known as the "Manhattan District" or "Project," this establishment took over complete control of the program from OSRD in April, 1943.

The Manhattan Project was a unique experience for all concerned. The Corps of Engineers was formally in control but performed only a fraction of the actual work. Army engineers chose locations and arranged supply for various facilities but the facilities themselves were constructed by private firms and operated mainly by academic and industrial scientists and engineers. General Groves, assisted by Colonels Kenneth D. Nichols and Franklin T.

Matthias, faced the increasingly difficult task of allocating support and making certain that the various phases of the project were properly correlated. When work would lag, General Groves would intervene to help clear the confusion, to counsel in risky decisions, and sometimes, where nothing else would avail, simply to urge on.

Otherwise, however, the scientists and engineers were on their own. Bush and Conant kept careful watch on the progress of the work, stepping in to offer advice, recruit personnel and mediate between the Project and the universities and private industry. Eger V. Murphree, a chemical engineer and Vice President of the Standard Oil Co., supervised engineering for research activities prior to production as chairman of the OSRD Planning Board. A. H. Compton, E. O. Lawrence, and Harold Urey were each put in charge of an alternative method for producing fissionable material. Of comparable importance was the role assigned to J. Robert Oppenheimer as Director of the Los Alamos Laboratory where the actual construction of the bomb was assigned.

The industrial contractors affiliated with the Project were also represented, for the most part, by engineers, some of whom worked on the Project while others served on committees of review. Among these were Crawford H. Greenewalt, G. B. Yancey, G. M. Evans, and Roger Williams of DuPont, Oliver E. Buckley of Bell Laboratories, Charles A. Thomas of Monsanto, William D. Coolidge, retired from General Electric, L. W. Chubb of Westinghouse, Percival C. Keith and George E. Curme of Union Carbide.

The laboratories at Chicago and Los Alamos brought together the heaviest concentrations of eminent academic scientists. Among those gathered under A. H. Compton in Chicago were physicists Fermi, Szilard, Samuel K. Allison, John A. Wheeler and Wigner, and chemists George P. Boyd, Charles C. Coryell, James Franck, and Glenn T. Seaborg. A number of the Chicago group moved on to Los Alamos when their most pressing immediate tasks were completed. Los Alamos attracted a host of brilliant scientists in every field, including Luis W. Alvarez, Robert F. Bacher, Kenneth T. Bainbridge, Hans Bethe, George B. Kistiakowsky, Charles C. Lauritsen, John Von Neumann, Norman F. Ramsey and Cyril S. Smith. A sizeable British delegation included Sir James Chadwick and Rudolf Peierls. Still others, like Jesse W. Beams at the University of Virginia and Frank H. Spedding at Iowa State College, pursued their work more or less in isolation.

If the scientists were largely on their own in the conduct of the work, the Manhattan Project itself stood virtually in a state of splendid isolation with respect to the government. Under the peculiar conditions imposed by the War, the Project was insulated not only against detailed executive control but also and even more from Congressional oversight. It was not until 1944 that the War Department decided it had become necessary to take into its confidence the majority and minority leaders of Congress as well as the leading members of the Appropriations Committees in both houses. With their cooperation, the funds requested by the Department for unspecified military purposes continued to be voted without requests for explanation.

It is no small tribute to all those who had a part in it, and particularly to the scores of scientists and engineers, that somehow, despite unforeseeable difficulties and the inevitable blind alleys, overall target dates were met. On occasion friction would arise between industrial engineers and academic scientists, between groups attached to alternate processes, between scientists and security officers, but cooperation far overshadowed conflict. Plainly the scientific community was united in its determination to put the defense of the nation ahead of all else. In the absence of this determination it may well be doubted whether any degree of external supervision and control would have accomplished the same results.

The Use of the Bomb: First Misgivings

By the time the first atomic explosive device was successfully tested at Almagordo in July, 1945, the world situation had changed dramatically and the fears which had first motivated scientists to press for the development of the atomic bomb were rendered obsolete. Until the very end of German resistance, the scientists did not know whether their enemy counterparts were ahead of them. When they finally discovered that the Germans were not even close behind, many of the scientists grew uneasy. Until then, fear lest

Hitler receive the bomb first had overridden moral misgivings. Now, those who had an idea of the destructive capacity of the new weapon had to face the question of whether, even in the hands of the democracies, it might still prove a danger to civilization. As they had once decided to press the weapon on the government, some scientists now urged the government not to use it and to make every effort to secure international control of atomic energy.

Early in May, an "Interim Committee," so designated in the expectation that, after the War, Congress would establish a permanent agency, was convened by President Truman to advise him on policy issues that might arise in connection with atomic research. Secretary of War Henry L. Stimson headed the Committee of high civilian officials. Their most pressing concern was the question of whether and in what way the atomic bomb should be used in the war.[11] Seven of the leading scientists participated in the deliberations. Three—Bush, Conant, and Karl T. Compton— were members of the eight-man Interim Committee; the others— Fermi, Oppenheimer, Lawrence, and A. H. Compton—were named to one of the two panels appointed to advise the committee, the "Scientific Panel." After deliberation the Interim Committee decided to recommend the use of the bomb against Japan. According to Secretary Stimson's account, the Committee was persuaded that especially in view of the proven tenacity of Japanese troops elsewhere, the planned invasion of the home islands of the enemy would inevitably demand a tremendous sacrifice of life. Military advisers did not believe that the bomb would produce damage any greater than would result from continuous saturation-bombings of Japan's congested, flammable cities. (They were using estimates of the scientists which later proved much too low, but not so low as to invalidate the conclusion.) But they did believe that the psychological effect of such damage from a single bomb would be far

---

[11] The principal works consulted for this account of the decision to use the atomic bomb are: Henry L. Stimson, "The Decision to Use the Atomic Bomb," *Harper's Magazine* (February 1947); A. H. Compton, *Atomic Quest* (New York: Oxford University Press, 1956); Alice Kimball Smith, "Behind the Decision to Use the Atomic Bomb, 1944-45," *BAS*, Vol. XIV, No. 8 (October 1958), pp. 288-312; Robert J. C. Butow, *Japan's Decision to Surrender* (Stanford: Stanford University Press, 1954); Herbert Feis, *Japan Subdued, The Atomic Bomb and the End of the Pacific War* (Princeton: Princeton University Press, 1961).

greater. They hoped that the shock of atomic bombing would induce the Japanese people to demand an immediate end to their
hopeless struggle.

Although attentive from the start to the proposal for a nonmilitary demonstration of the weapon, the Committee declared
itself unable to conceive of any exhibition that would have as high
a probability of effectiveness as an actual bombing. If the bomb
put on exhibit proved to be a dud, Japanese morale might well be
bolstered. Even if the test were successfully conducted in some
remote area, the Japanese military might choose to deceive their
people as to the extent of damage caused, and fissionable materials
in short supply would have been wasted. Some felt that even a
successful test in the ocean or on a desert island, where physical
damage would be minimal, might not make enough of an impres-
sion on observers. If an area in Japan were selected as the site of a
demonstration and the choice announced in advance, air defense
might prove an obstacle and Allied prisoners might be moved in.
These and other conjectures led the participants in the meetings
of both the Committee and the Panel to conclude that a demonstration was an impractical alternative.

While the Committee was deliberating, scientists engaged in the
Manhattan District were discussing the issue among themselves. At
the "Metallurgical Laboratory" attached to the University of
Chicago, a "Committee on Social and Political Implications" had
been formed under the chairmanship of James Franck. The group
issued a document which came to be known as the "Franck Report"
arguing that by using the bomb we would sow such distrust of the
United States that after the War we would find it extremely difficult to have atomic weapons outlawed by international agreement.
The report urged that instead of putting the bomb to military use
we arrange a special demonstration to emphasize its extraordinary
character. A petition to this effect was circulated among the scientific personnel of the laboratory and gained a number of signatures.
In order to provide a more representative mirror of opinion, a
poll was then conducted under other auspices. The results were
taken to indicate that a majority approved military use, but the
propositions voted on were not altogether unambiguous. Although
only a small number were unqualifiedly opposed to any military

use, the largest number of respondents favored what was identified only as a "military demonstration." The substance of the Franck proposals was considered by the Scientific Panel, which met over a weekend at Los Alamos (probably June 9 and 10) at the request of the Interim Committee, to consider again the feasibility of a demonstration. The four scientists concluded it was hopeless. "We can propose," they admitted, "no technical demonstration likely to bring an end to the war; we see no acceptable alternative to direct military use." [12]

The decision to drop the bomb has been criticized on a number of grounds. It has been argued with the support of the U.S. Strategic Bombing Survey conducted shortly after the War, that continued saturation bombing would soon have brought the Japanese to surrender. It has been alleged that the bomb was used chiefly because the Truman administration was anxious to prove, in anticipation of postwar investigation, that the vast sums spent developing the weapon had not been spent in vain. Similarly it has been suggested that the decision was taken largely to make unnecessary the active entry of the Soviet Union into the Pacific War or to strengthen our hand in the negotiation of postwar settlements. The first criticism must remain conjectural. The second two were at most minor considerations. Secretary of State James F. Byrnes was concerned with the possibility that if the bomb did not work a Congressional investigation would prove embarrassing, but he suggested only that the project be reviewed by the executive first. The attitude of the government toward the entry of the Soviet Union into the Pacific War did become less insistent after the bomb became available, but the issue was given little consideration in connection with the decision to employ the bomb.

Tragic as it was, the decision to drop the bomb does not seem so susceptible to criticism in itself as it is in the larger context of Allied policy. Had there been no insistence on unconditional surrender and had the Japanese been specifically offered the right to decide for themselves whether to keep the Emperor, the peace party which eventually won out might have succeeded in time to preclude atomic bombing, especially if the Japanese had been informed that we had the bomb and were ready to use it.

[12] Henry L. Stimson, "The Decision to Use the Atomic Bomb," p. 101.

The seven scientists, like the others involved in the decision, only considered the narrower question. They were in no position, in terms either of their advisory role or of their political-military understanding, to take a more comprehensive view. No other development indicated so clearly as this first test how ill-prepared were scientists to assume the functions of statesman and strategist. Nothing in their training had prepared them for these new functions. In reporting their inability to devise a practical demonstration, the advisory panel observed that scientists "have no claim to special competence in solving the political, social and military problems which are presented by the advent of atomic power." [13] For some, this frank abdication may have served as a shield to deflect any charge of personal irresponsibility. For others, it stood as an accusing commentary on the scientists' failure. Having once imagined themselves young Prometheans they now felt like adolescent arsonists who had begun to play with fire and were now unable to control it.

The Curious Case of the German Physicists

Because the atom had first been split experimentally in Germany and because of the well-earned reputation of German scientists, the refugee physicists who gathered in England and America worried throughout the War that Germany might be ahead in the race for the bomb. As the War in Europe was ending, worry only increased lest the Germans produce the bomb in time to use it as a desperation weapon. To find out what in fact was happening, an American team of investigators, identified in code as Alsos (Greek for "groves"), was assigned the mission of seeking out and interrogating German scientists. Samuel Goudsmit, later to become director of the Brookhaven National Laboratory, directed the operation in conjunction with Colonel Boris T. Pash, who had been assigned to the Los Alamos Laboratory as chief security officer. They found, much to the relief of the Allies, that the Germans had made very little progress in developing atomic energy and could not yet give serious attention to the production of a bomb. In

[13] *Ibid.*

1945 they were still engaged in experiments to produce a controlled chain reaction such as Fermi had achieved in 1940.

Why were the Germans so far behind? According to Goudsmit the captured German scientists first decried the news of the atomic bomb as Allied propaganda. They "were so sure of their own superiority it never occurred to them that we might have succeeded where they had failed." Then, when it became apparent that such a bomb had actually been produced, they were plunged into dismay and mutual recrimination. Some of the younger men reproached their elders for having failed the fatherland. Walter Gerlach, the director of war projects, "acted like a defeated general" and remained depressed for several days. Only afterward, according to Goudsmit, did they hit upon "a brilliant rationalization of their failure." They would contend that they had worked exclusively on a "uranium machine" and had not even tried to make so horrible a thing as an atomic bomb. This was half true, but "only because they failed to understand the difference between the machine and the bomb." They were attempting, in other words, to develop a pile that could be dropped as a bomb. Except for a suggestive paper written by Fritz Houtermans but ignored by the Heisenberg "clique" because Houtermans was an outsider, the Germans had no inkling that a new element, plutonium, might be produced and used as material for a bomb.[14]

More recently a different account has been provided by Robert Jungk setting forth the version favored by the circle of physicists around Heisenberg. According to Jungk, "they did not push for the construction of such a bomb. . . . On the contrary, these physicists were able successfully to divert the minds of the National Socialist Service Departments from the idea of so inhuman a weapon." Not only Houtermans but Carl F. von Weizsäcker, both of them as early as 1940, are said to have committed to paper the idea that a new element, called by von Weizsäcker Element 93, might be produced in a uranium pile and might be explosive. In order to keep such ideas quiet, according to Jungk, the Heisenberg group had to make it appear they were technically impractical. Though not a member of the group, Houtermans asserts he knew of their desire to keep the government in the dark on the subject

[14] Samuel A. Goudsmit, *Alsos, the Story of a Mission,* pp. 133-39, 178-79.

and agreed to it. He only permitted publication of the paper in 1944 when the idea was broached in another German publication. Heisenberg, caught between his commitments to his nation and his dislike of the Nazis, visited Niels Bohr in occupied Copenhagen late in 1941 with the intention of proposing through Bohr to the scientists abroad that they all refrain from providing such a weapon to either side. Heisenberg asserts that his caution in broaching the subject obscured the purpose of his visit and only succeeded in arousing Bohr's fear that Hitler would benefit from such a weapon. According to his own account, Heisenberg also suggested in that conversation that "a decay product of U-239" could be produced to serve as an explosive.[15]

Jungk's contribution makes the record as complete as it is likely ever to be, but it remains difficult to draw a judgment upon it with certainty. Are the accounts of the German scientists, not only of their scientific knowledge but of their motives, to be credited in major part or dismissed as *post hoc* rationalizations? Did they consider the creation of plutonium likely or merely possible? Did they always oppose the regime or did they grow firmly opposed only when the war seemed hopelessly lost? Was opposition so widespread, for so long, as to prevent other German physicists from exploring the possibilities? Eugene Rabinowitch's balanced judgment is well worth considering:

> I believe that the conspiracy of German scientists not to give the atomic bomb to Hitler, as described by Jungk, is a *post factum* rationalization of a vague uneasiness which caused German scientists to drag their feet, rather than to put into the atomic bomb work the same enthusiasm and urgency that animated their British and American colleagues. The German scientists, while not outright defeatists, had not the same fear of Hitler's defeat as the Western scientists had of a German victory. They grasped at evidence that the bomb could not be made in time for use in the war; and their a-scientific, if not anti-scientific officialdom did little to urge them on.[16]

But wherever the truth lies, enough evidence has been produced in the effort to exculpate the German scientists to suggest to American

[15] Robert Jungk, *Brighter than a Thousand Suns*, pp. 88-104.
[16] Eugene Rabinowitch, "Responsibilities of Scientists in the Atomic Age" *BAS*, Vol. XV, No. 1 (January 1959), p. 3.

scientists an uncomfortable reversal of roles. In the flush of victory they were inclined to take pleasure in having beaten the Germans to it. Later they seemed to stand accused of failing to exercise moral restraint while "Hitler's scientists" appeared to have been guided by humanitarian considerations.

6

THE POLITICS OF DECISION

As the atomic bombing of Hiroshima and Nagasaki brought the War to a dramatic end, those who had worked in the Manhattan District and even those who were identified with its achievement only as members of scientific and engineering professions suddenly found themselves in an altogether anomalous position.

In the eyes of the public they were heroes of a sort, credited with a major contribution to victory. Having created so awesome an instrument of power, they could no longer be dismissed as mere tinkerers or fuzzy theorists. Nor could their achievement be assimilated under the conventional canons of personal enterprise which had been applied to inventors like Bell, Edison, and Ford. To the government, especially to those in the executive who appreciated the growing importance of science, they had become a major source of national power and a new group to be reckoned with in the formulation of policy. Almost overnight leading scientists emerged as respected public figures. As the director of the Manhattan Project Metallurgical Laboratory in Chicago, Samuel K. Allison, recalled later,

> Suddenly physicists were exhibited as lions at Washington tea-parties, were invited to conventions of social scientists, where their opinions on society were respectfully listened to by life-long experts in the field, attended conventions of religious orders and discoursed on theology, were asked to endorse plans for world government, and to give simplified lectures on the nucleus to Congressional committees.[1]

Scientists were not held in uniformly high regard at the upper echelons of the military hierarchies. Yet there were some professional

[1] Samuel K. Allison, "The State of Physics; Or the Perils of Being Important," *BAS*, Vol. VI, No. 1 (January 1950), p. 3.

soldiers who recognized that the war experience was only the first phase of a new and permanent connection between the sciences of nature and the arts of war.

To themselves, however, scientists appeared rather less heroic. As Oppenheimer has said, in a classic comment that expressed a feeling no doubt widespread: "In some sense, which no vulgarity, no humor, no overstatement can quite extinguish, the physicists have known sin and this is a knowledge which they cannot lose." Philip Morrison, in an address reprinted in the newly founded *Bulletin of the Atomic Physicists* of Chicago, recalled the words of a Japanese radiologist who had survived Hiroshima: "I did the experiment years ago, but only on a few rats. But you Americans— you are wonderful. You have made the human experiment." "No one," wrote Morrison, "could fail to carry the scar of such a cutting thrust." [2]

Some scientists felt such intense guilt, mingled with anger at the politicians they accused of misusing their creativity and ignoring their counsel, that they decided to withdraw: to keep from publication whatever findings might have military applications, to refuse to work on military projects, and in some cases to restrict themselves to research in fields with no direct bearing upon weapons of destruction. In 1946 Norbert Wiener of M.I.T. made public his refusal to honor an Air Force request for a reprint of a paper in which he had discussed problems relevant to guided missiles. In the past, he wrote, scientists had given their knowledge freely to all who asked, but the bombing of Hiroshima and Nagasaki had made it clear that "to provide scientific information is not a necessarily innocent act, and may entail the gravest consequences." Wiener continued: "The experience of the scientists who have worked on the atomic bomb has indicated that in any investigation of this kind, the scientist ends by putting unlimited power in the hands of the people he is least inclined to trust with [its] use." The only responsible course was to refuse to be implicated. "To disseminate information about a weapon in the present state of our civilization is to make it practically certain that that weapon will be used." [3]

[2] Philip Morrison, "The Laboratory Demobilizes," *BAS*, Vol. II, Nos. 9 and 10 (November 1946), pp. 5-6.

[3] The letter appeared originally in *The Atlantic Monthly* (December 1946), and was reprinted in the *BAS*, Vol. III, No. 1 (January 1947), p. 31.

At the other extreme were those who would have pursued their work not without misgiving but with an ultimate confidence in the benefits of science. As Edward Teller put it,

> It is the duty of those of us who made the first atomic bombs to find out all the dangers and all the terrors of our discovery. We have eaten of the tree of knowledge, and as scientists we must have the faith—perhaps the temerity—to believe that knowledge in the end will be turned to blessing. At least we should have the conviction that if we should give way to fear and if we should fail to explore the limits of human power we shall surely be lost.[4]

By no means all or even most of the interested scientists followed Wiener into principled withdrawal or Teller into total commitment. For many it was in any case an academic question. With the War over, scientists left wartime labs in droves in order to return to their civilian careers and homes. Nor was the government greatly concerned to stop the exodus. In this, as in other respects, the focus of attention had shifted from war to peace. But even though they were for the time being removed from direct concern with weapons development, it rapidly became apparent that many scientists were determined not to ignore the military applications of science. Among these, the largest group would seem to have decided that the most important question was not whether to develop new weapons but how to influence what was done with the deadly instruments that had already been furnished. They were to learn that this special responsibility, although a plainly felt pressure, was not easily defined or implemented. What "rights" did their authorship confer, if any? What policies were the responsible ones? What channels, institutional and informal, ought they to make use of? If they were to retain the confidence of government and public, would they not have to answer any future call to military research?

Renewal and Response

The corporate entry of scientists into postwar politics was in part made easier by the prior renewal of the tradition of scientific

[4] Edward Teller, "Atomic Scientists Have Two Responsibilities," *BAS*, Vol. III, No. 12 (December 1947), pp. 335-336.

fellowship inherited from Europe and assimilated in the experience of the War. The commitment to science had been reinforced by the brilliant accomplishments of the War period, which brought to fruition much that had only been dreamt of earlier. Especially in the physical sciences a spirit of common dedication had grown up in America reminiscent of the prewar European ideal. Exemplary scientists and teachers like Oppenheimer, Lawrence, A. H. Compton, and Conant played the role in America that Bohr, Rutherford, Heisenberg, and others played in Europe. With atomic energy a reality there was now more reason than ever to see science as the most exalted of human activities, as the key to economic abundance and even to international brotherhood.

Yet even as they drew upon the old traditions, a new sense of uneasiness led the scientists to recognize an immediate social responsibility. Whereas previously politics had entered the laboratory only as an unwelcome intruder, now the same laboratory served as a political clubroom. Spontaneously scientists came together at the wartime centers to form associations, many of which soon merged in the Federation of Atomic Scientists, later amalgamated with the Federation of American Scientists. In 1950 a smaller number was to be enrolled by the Society for Social Responsibility in Science, organized by pacifists to bring together scientists who refrained from military work as "conscientious objectors." Chicago, where the Franck Report originated, now served as the publishing center for the renamed *Bulletin of Atomic Scientists*. On the cover of the *Bulletin,* when it acquired one, along with a magazine format, appeared a clock symbolizing approaching atomic doom, the hands originally indicating fifteen minutes to midnight. The editors have since taken note of significant developments by moving the minute hand. By 1953, with both the United States and the Soviet Union in possession of hydrogen bombs, the hands were moved forward to two minutes to midnight. Only recently, in recognition of widening concern with the dangers of nuclear war, have the editors moved the minute hand back to five minutes.

In the *Bulletin* the scientists formulated their policies in intramural exchange, keeping abreast of scientific and political news, and reaching out to laymen who shared their concerns. The Federation opened what was described as a "cubbyhole" in Washington where scientists would report for assignments in Congressional lobbying and public education. Thus outfitted with a publication of their own and with an organization, the atomic scientists led the effort to transform the sense of special responsibility into a pattern of political activity.

The Scientist as Lobbyist

The first efforts of scientists to influence public policy were directed toward the legislative consideration of proposals for an agency to support scientific research and for a commission to supervise the development of atomic energy.

Support for research became an issue with the introduction of bills in the Senate designed to enact the recommendations of Vannevar Bush's *Science, The Endless Frontier*. The bill offered by Senator Warren Magnuson of Washington would have created a National Research Foundation governed by a nine-man board. It was understood that members of the board would be drawn principally from among eminent scientists and that the board would operate without formal executive control. In addition it was provided that wartime practices with respect to patents were to remain in force: companies would continue to be allowed to patent results of work supported in whole or part by federal funds unless specifically restricted by the terms of the contract.

Another bill submitted by Senator Harley M. Kilgore of West Virginia on behalf of a subcommittee of the Committee on Military Affairs called for a foundation to be directed by an administrator appointed by the President and advised by a large board. The Kilgore bill would have placed a blanket prohibition on the issuance of patents for devices stemming from government-sponsored research. It would also have required that research grants be distributed according to a formula designed to provide aid to smaller colleges and universities throughout the nation as well as to the major academic research centers. The Kilgore bill also provided for support of the social sciences by the foundation, whereas the Magnuson bill contained no specific provision for such support.

As Talcott Parsons pointed out at the time in a suggestive

sociological commentary,[5] the scientists interested in the foundation split into two groups. One comprised those who had been on the "inside" of wartime agencies like the OSRD or were associated as administrators with the private institutions or contractors who carried out the work. This group preferred that the wartime arrangements be perpetuated to enable industry and the universities to work with government in an informal partnership free from political interference and control. The opinions of the group were represented by the Committee to Support the Bush Report, headed by President Isaiah Bowman of Johns Hopkins, and by Bush himself.

The other group, more broadly based, had as its chief spokesmen scientists Harold Urey and Harlow Shapley. Without criticizing the wartime arrangement, those in this second camp took the view that to perpetuate it would be to encourage oligopoly in industry and education. They also contended that the method of organization which had been effective in promoting applied research was not so well suited to the different job of supporting basic research. The Kilgore bill appealed to them because it put the foundation under the supervision of the executive. Only if the government were assured more authority than private industry and institutions, they believed, would the public interest in basic research be adequately served. For the same reason they also approved the provision of the Kilgore bill denying patent rights to industry, in order to discourage the use of foundation funds for applied, commercially-oriented research rather than for genuine fundamental science. The social science issue, though marginal, found this group taking a broader, more humanistic view of science in contrast to the more exclusive concern for natural sciences taken by the Bush-Bowman group and reflected in the silence of the Magnuson bill on this subject.

Although ideologically and in practical institutional terms these two positions were sharply at variance, both groups proved not so committed to them as to be willing to watch the legislative debate drag on inconclusively while their differences were exploited by those

[5] Talcott Parsons, "National Science Legislation, Part 1: An Historical Review," *BAS*, Vol. II, Nos. 9 and 10 (November 1946), pp. 7-8.

in Congress opposed to any foundation. By 1950, after other efforts had failed and one bill had been vetoed, they agreed to support a compromise bill acceptable to the Truman administration. The foundation was to be governed by a director appointed by the President and a board with limited power. Patents were not prohibited and no specific provision was made for support of the social sciences. The rationale behind the bill as it emerged in this form was pragmatic and administrative rather than ideological. The office of director was placed within the executive in order to strengthen the position of the agency in the competition for appropriations and not in order to forestall the influence of private interests. Patents were permitted, but only to encourage industry to give more attention to basic research as the foundation would define it.

Although neither group could be wholly satisfied with the outcome of this issue, scientists would appear to have been more united and more successful in the somewhat similar matter of the Atomic Energy Commission. In 1945 spokesmen for scientists successfully raised opposition to the May-Johnson bill, sponsored by the War Department. The Department and the House Committee on Military Affairs were accused of trying to railroad the bill through Congress and of ignoring the opinions of scientists. Among other provisions, the bill called for a part-time commission with twelve members: five scientists and engineers to be nominated by the NAS, three other civilians to be appointed by the President, and two Army and two Navy representatives. Leading scientists at first joined Secretary of War Robert Patterson and General Groves to urge swift passage of the bill. Bush and Conant testified with military leaders at a one-day hearing held by the House Committee. Publication of the provisions of the bill, however, raised a storm of protest from scientists in Chicago, led by Szilard, and soon also from Los Alamos. The bill, it was charged, was not being given adequate consideration and the proposed commission was bound to be one in which the military representatives would wield predominant power.

While A. H. Compton reserved judgment, three members of the Interim Committee Scientific Panel, Fermi, Lawrence, and Oppenheimer, rushed to reassure the scientific community that the bill had been carefully and wisely drawn up. But when the scientists who had endorsed the bill had a chance to examine it closely, all of them lost their perfect assurance. The severe restrictions and harsh penalties of the security provisions met with universal disapproval. Although Oppenheimer nevertheless testified in favor of the bill, it became plain that many scientists would oppose passage bitterly and vigorously.

In the Senate, meanwhile, the co-author of the bill, Senator Edwin C. Johnson of Colorado, ran into other, more immediately effective, opposition. Led by Senator Arthur Vandenberg of Michigan, the Senate refused to refer the subject of atomic energy to the Military Affairs Committee on the ground that it was only in part a matter of military concern. Instead the Senate accepted the proposal offered by Senator Brien McMahon of Connecticut for a Special Senate Committee to hold hearings into the subject and recommend appropriate legislation.

Named to chair the Special Committee, McMahon appointed Edward U. Condon, the physicist, as scientific adviser to the Committee and James R. Newman, a lawyer serving with the Office of Defense Mobilization and Reconversion, as special counsel. Newman and another government lawyer, Byron S. Miller, sought the advice of scientists and others in the government who were, like themselves, not satisfied with the May-Johnson bill. They drafted an alternative for the Committee, accepting modifications from executive agencies and in the process gaining important support. In a memorandum to the President prepared from a study of the problem by Don K. Price, Harold D. Smith, the Director of the Bureau of the Budget, pointed out that while the May-Johnson commission was deliberately designed to exclude executive interference, the new bill gave the President substantial instruments of control. Truman, who had earlier endorsed the May-Johnson bill, withdrew his support after further consideration and indicated his approval of the McMahon bill.

While the new bill was being drafted and re-drafted, the scientists turned the heat of public opinion upon Congress. The FAS and a broader *ad hoc* organization, the National Committee for Atomic Information, led a highly successful campaign involving forums, publicity and letter-writing, to drum up support for civilian control and to gain passage of the bill.

As finally made law, the Atomic Energy Act provided for a civilian commission of five members appointed by the President with the consent of the Senate and for a general manager, to head the staff of the commission, also to be appointed by the President. The commission would be assisted by two advisory boards, one composed of scientists (the General Advisory Committee), the other of representatives of the Armed Services (the Military Liaison Committee). Congress was to keep abreast of the work of the Commission through a Joint Congressional Committee on Atomic Energy and it was understood that the President would maintain regular contact through the Chairman of the Commission.

Scientists wanted to keep the development of atomic energy out of exclusively military control because of their desire to see atomic energy turned to peaceful purposes. A similar concern engaged them in the effort to put atomic energy under international control. Secretary Byrnes asked his Under Secretary, Dean Acheson, to head a committee also to include Bush, Conant, McCloy, and Groves, which was to draft proposals for international negotiation. Acheson in turn appointed a board of technical consultants to provide the initial basis for the proposals. David E. Lilienthal, afterward to become the first chairman of the AEC, served as chairman of the Board, with Carroll Wilson of OSRD as Secretary and Herbert S. Marks, Acheson's special assistant, as adviser. The other members of the board were Chester I. Barnard, prominent executive with New Jersey Bell Telephone, Oppenheimer, Charles A. Thomas, and Harry A. Winne of General Electric. The result was the Acheson-Lilienthal report and the proposals put forward on the basis of the report by Bernard Baruch in the United Nations. The proposals were based on the belief that a workable system of inspection would not be likely to gain acceptance but that it would be feasible to put under international ownership and supervision all "dangerous" atomic activities.* An Atomic Develop-

---

* Only later was the distinction between safe and dangerous recognized to be impractical. This development unfortunately left the American negotiators open to the propagandistic charge that they were retreating from their earlier position. The consultants have since been criticized for having been so eager to promote an agreement that they gave advice based upon inadequate technical investigation. See Robert G. Gard, "Arms Control Policy Formulation and Negotiation 1945-46" (Ph.D. thesis, Harvard University, 1961). It should be noted, however, that they took care to point out that further research might show the technique of "denaturing" explosive atomic materials to be ineffective.

ment Authority would manage the facilities which were to be deliberately dispersed throughout the world to prevent any one nation from seizing the facilities and turning them to military purposes.

In themselves the Baruch proposals represented at least a fresh approach to the international stalemate, and for this the scientists deserve part of the credit. The approach did not succeed because each side had reservations which the other was unprepared to accommodate. The Russians seem to have had no intention of negotiating in earnest until they had atomic capacities and a stockpile of their own. The United States was unwilling to destroy its stockpile before an authority was firmly established or to accept a veto power in the application of sanctions to violators of an agreement. Two weeks after Baruch made public the American proposals, the United States carried out an atomic bomb test at Bikini to gauge the effectiveness of the weapon in naval warfare. The unfortunate timing of the two events raised the suspicion, however unjustified, that the Baruch proposals were insincere and an effort merely to preserve our advantage in atomic weapons. When it became obvious that the long series of talks had degenerated entirely into occasions for propaganda, Harold Urey expressed the sense of disillusionment that he and his colleagues experienced: "As scientists we have engaged in an experiment in international control of the atomic bomb, and today it seems to me that we should realize that the experiment is a failure." [6]

In this instance as in the others, scientists tasted a power to influence agencies of government, but their successes fell far short of their goals. A National Science Foundation was in being but on terms that many found precarious and unsatisfactory. International control of atomic energy was no nearer and the opportunity for it seemed likely only to diminish with time. The Atomic Energy Commission had been established as a civilian agency but many of those who fought for the McMahon Act were deeply disappointed with the comparatively minute attention paid by the AEC to the application of atomic energy to peaceful purposes. Military applications claimed by far the larger share of attention, despite civilian control.

In other, lasting respects, however, scientists gained much from

[6] Harold Urey, "An Alternative Course for the Control of Atomic Energy," *BAS*, Vol. III, No. 6 (June 1947), p. 139.

their political activity. They learned that in some matters they stood together as scientists, while in others they divided with the rest of the nation, as in matters touching the role of governmental and private enterprise, to take the key example. By testing their strength they discovered some of its limitations. By pursuing ultimate goals they raised a standard for others. From their small success they learned also to appreciate some of the difficulties of politics and not to disparage the virtues of pragmatic politicians.

The Scientist as Strategist

Having experienced the limitations of legislative lobbying, the scientists turned to a more direct approach to the centers of decision-making. From the open halls of Congress they moved to the closed corridors of the Pentagon. In order to advance the cause of peace, scientists had all but ignored strategic policy and weapons development, directing their attention instead to efforts seeking settlements and arms control agreements. Reluctantly they grew to realize that as the possibilities of radical change grew more and more remote, the prospects of peace would depend increasingly on the immediate issues of military and foreign policy. Hand in hand with this shift of concern came a renewed interest in the military application of science from within the government. As a result, scientists again found access to the centers of executive decision.

For a considerable time after the War, production and development of atomic weapons proceeded slowly and without repercussions on military planning. Even then there was some feeling, especially in the Services, that the pace was dangerously slow. The Navy would have liked to encourage the development of a smaller bomb suitable for delivery by carrier-based aircraft. But it required as much fissionable material to make a small bomb as it did to make a large one. As long as production continued to be slow and costly, the economics of nuclear power seemed to dictate production of the large bomb. For a time the Army also resigned itself to a nonatomic future. The Air Force, free from the pressure of competition from either of the other Services, rested securely upon its monopoly of the bomb, and concentrated on developing improved methods of delivery. The policy of the Joint Chiefs of Staff was simply to continue to stockpile atomic bombs.[7]

At the Los Alamos Laboratory major stress continued to fall upon the effort to make the bomb more efficient and to increase the quantity of explosive it could contain before a critical mass was reached. Tests at Eniwetok in 1948 resulted in a bomb six times more destructive than that used at Hiroshima. Air Force strategists were gratified by these results because they believed that in a future war it would be more difficult than ever for bombers to penetrate enemy defenses. It would therefore be better to gamble on delivering a few large bombs than on delivering a great number of smaller bombs.

The attitude of strategic comfort induced by this slow but substantial progress was rudely challenged late in the summer of 1949 when government scientists deduced from a number of indicies that the Russians had tested, without publicity but with apparent success, an atomic weapon of their own. The Soviet "Joe I" shot caused consternation among those responsible for our program, especially since it came in the context of worsening relations between the United States and the Soviet Union. Once again, scientists were urged to turn their attention to weapons development.

This time, however, it was not clear in what directions they ought to go. As early as 1942 it had been thought possible to develop a bomb of much larger magnitude by going, as Assistant Secretary of Defense John J. McCloy put it in 1946, to the other end of the periodic table. Even during the Manhattan Project, Edward Teller had chosen to work on this more advanced phase of development well before the atomic bomb was an accomplished fact. But it was not until "Joe I" that work on a thermonuclear weapon (so called because fusion would be activated by the heat of fission explosion) was begun in earnest.

When the news of the Soviet shot became known, political agitation for the "Super" arose within Congress. William L. Borden, the executive Director of the Joint Committee on Atomic Energy, reportedly called the attention of members of the Committee to the possibilities that had already been mentioned. At the same time,

[7] The account in this and the following paragraph draws upon Ralph E. Lapp, *The New Force* (New York: Harper & Brothers, 1953), pp. 116-118.

scientists who knew of these possibilities entered into independent deliberations. At the University of California at Berkeley, E. O. Lawrence, Wendell Latimer, and Edward Teller—soon to be aided by others, including Luis W. Alvarez, the physicist, and Kenneth S. Pitzer, the chemist—decided among themselves to press for a full-scale effort to develop the new bomb. They went first to the AEC where they reportedly met with a cool reception from Chairman Lilienthal and received their only warm support from Admiral Lewis Strauss. Strauss recommended that they take their case to Senator McMahon and to Senator Bourke Hickenlooper of Iowa, majority and minority leaders of the JCAE. They also sought out old scientific collaborators, but found reactions mixed. Hans Bethe, whose studies of solar heat had contributed greatly to existing knowledge upon which the theoretical possibilities of fusion were based, indicated interest but declined to go to work on the bomb at that time. Others expressed vigorous opposition. Conant wrote Oppenheimer that such a bomb would be produced "over my dead body." Oppenheimer responded in similar terms of dismay and repugnance in a letter addressed to "Uncle Jim."

> What concerns me is really not the technical problem. I am not sure the miserable thing will work, nor that it can be gotten to a target except by ox cart. It seems likely to me even further to worsen the unbalance of our present war plans. What does worry me is that this thing appears to have caught the imagination, both of the congressional and of military people, as the answer to the problem posed by the Russian advance. It would be folly to oppose the exploration of this weapon. We have always known it had to be done; and it does have to be done, though it appears to be singularly proof against any form of experimental approach. But that we become committed to it as the way to save the country and the peace appears to me full of dangers.[8]

Conant and Oppenheimer were not alone among scientists in reacting with no or little enthusiasm to the bid for a crash program to develop the H-bomb. In October 1949 the AEC broached the

---

[8] Quoted in *In the Matter of J. Robert Oppenheimer, Transcript of a Hearing Before Personnel Security Board, Washington, April 12, 1954, through May 6, 1954* (Washington, D.C.: Government Printing Office, 1954), pp. 242-243. Hereafter cited as *Oppenheimer Transcript*.

question to its General Advisory Committee. Present were Oppenheimer and Conant, Lee DuBridge, President of Cal Tech, Hartley Rowe, chief engineer of the United Fruit Co., Oliver E. Buckley, President of Bell Laboratories, Cyril S. Smith, Metallurgist at the University of Chicago, I. I. Rabi, physicist at Columbia, and Enrico Fermi. The Committee heard first from the Commissioners, then from George F. Kennan on behalf of the State Department, and General Omar Bradley, Admiral W. F. Parsons, and others for the Armed Services. Six of the nine members of the GAC (one, Glenn Seaborg, was absent) agreed that it would be unwise to undertake a crash program at the time. Even though they rated it a "better than even chance" that the bomb would prove feasible, they concluded that it would be inadvisable to divert from the production of atomic weapons the laboratories, personnel, reactors, and fissionable materials which would be required to produce it. It did not seem to the Committee that the results could possibly justify the effort. Why go beyond the destructive power already conferred by the atomic bomb? Of what use was an "overkill"? They could draw support from military advisers who were concerned that nothing impede a continued stockpiling of atomic weapons and who advised the Committee that only two potential Soviet targets (Moscow and Leningrad) require bombs more powerful than atomic bombs for almost total destruction. (As yet there apparently was no significant recognition that hydrogen bomb warheads might well be required if relatively inaccurate missiles rather than bombers were relied on for delivery.) With prospects for an H-bomb still in doubt, with the cost of rapid development bound to be steep and bound to divert resources from the production of atomic weapons, and with the weapons of such marginal value, the GAC members decided to counsel against a crash program.

Another consideration in the decision, and by no means a minor one, was the feeling among the members of the Committee that the development of so destructive a bomb was repugnant on moral grounds as well. Fermi and Rabi appended a minority report which differed somewhat in its conclusions but also stressed the moral consideration. The report noted the "danger to humanity as a whole" that such a bomb would present. It would be "necessarily an evil thing considered in any light." It was therefore "important for the

President of the United States to tell the American public and the world that we think [it] wrong on fundamental ethical principles to initiate the development of such a weapon." The new danger of this prospective weapon, they urged, made it all the more imperative to make unceasing efforts to end the Cold War. But the report differed from the majority opinion in concluding that, if new efforts were also unsuccessful, we would have no recourse but to step up work on an H-bomb.[9]

The AEC forwarded both reports along with one of its own to President Truman. All five members of the AEC agreed that the decision was so important that it ought to be made by the President himself. They also indicated that they felt themselves handicapped by a lack of information on three points: Would our decision affect the stalemate in the U.N.? (Could it be used, in other words, to bargain with the Russians?) How would our allies react to an affirmative decision? Would the new weapon add significantly to our military strength? Each member submitted his own comments along with the general observations. Two stood clearly opposed to an immediate crash program, pending another try at negotiation and pending further information in answer to the AEC's questions. Two were clearly in favor of a crash program as things stood, and one was opposed to any further dependence on ever larger bombs.

By the end of January 1950 the AEC received an answer from the executive. The State Department asserted that the decision would in no way seriously affect United Nations negotiations or the allegiance of our allies. The Defense Department replied that the bomb would confer clear military advantages. Every member of the AEC with the exception of Lilienthal thereupon gave assent to the projected crash program. President Truman appointed Secretary of State Acheson, Secretary of Defense Louis Johnson, and Mr. Lilienthal as a special subcommittee of the National Security Council to prepare a fresh report for him on the question of a crash program. With Lilienthal continuing in opposition, and the other two members deciding in favor, the subcommittee reported affirmatively on the program. On January 31 Truman ordered it put in effect. His decision was made against the immediate background of the announcement that an eminent physicist, Klaus

[9] *Ibid.*, Testimony of J. Robert Oppenheimer, pp. 79-80.

Fuchs, who had worked on the atomic bomb, had confessed to betraying secret information to the U.S.S.R. during the War.

While these deliberations were in process, scientists were dividing into hostile camps. Some were busy seeking support for the program in Congress and the executive and from the Armed Services. Others, finding themselves rebuffed within the government, were turning to other scientists and to the public. When the decision was announced, twelve scientists issued a public protest against the crash program. Bethe, who was among the twelve, warned that the H-bomb held a special radiation hazard because of the long half-life of Carbon-14. Oppenheimer decried the atmosphere of secrecy in which such important decisions were being made without detailed public knowledge or understanding. Robert F. Bacher argued that the Armed Forces would scarcely know what to do with even a reasonably large supply of atomic bombs, if the time ever came when they might be needed.[10] Teller and his associates meanwhile moved to counter the effects of this opposition among scientists. In the *Bulletin* Teller issued a clarion call in an article entitled "Back to the Laboratory!" He compared the apathetic attitude among scientists to the complacency of the democracies in 1939 before an earlier totalitarian menace. Before it would again be too late, Teller urged, scientists must renovate the arsenal of democracy. "The honeymoon is over," he wrote. "H-bombs will not produce themselves. Neither will rockets nor radar. If we want to live on the technological capital of the last war, we shall come out second best." [11]

Not many months after Teller and those who responded to his call returned to the laboratories, other scientists at work on fission bombs made a discovery which permitted a great economy in the use of uranium as an explosive. As a result it was possible to speed production of small-scale weapons. This meant, it turned out, that the H-bomb would become entangled in a conflict among the Services. The Army contended that, with nuclear parity, Soviet superiority in ground forces could be neutralized only by tactical atomic weapons designed for battlefield use. Accordingly, in 1950 the Army initiated the development of an atomic shell in the 10-

---

[10] See the issues of the *BAS* for March, April, and May, 1950.
[11] *BAS*, Vol. VI, No. 3 (March 1950), pp. 71-72.

kiloton range which could be fired by howitzer. (The project was brought to successful completion in 1952.) Also developed were tactical atomic bombs compact enough to be carried by jet airplanes for battlefield use.

As a result of these developments the Army came to be identified with the cause of tactical atomic weapons, while the Air Force, especially the Strategic Air Command, became passionately committed to larger weapons and to the "ultimate" weapon, the H-bomb. Teller and his co-workers soon discovered the utility of the Air Force's concern. Having had long-standing difficulties with Norris Bradbury, Oppenheimer's successor as Director of Los Alamos, Teller requested a new laboratory from the AEC. His request was at first turned down by the AEC, then under a new Chairman, Gordon Dean, and he turned for help, on the advice of W. L. Borden, to the chief scientist of the Air Force, Louis Ridenour. With Ridenour, Teller discussed the possibility that the Air Force might support his request if its planners could be persuaded that their policy interests might benefit from his work. Meanwhile, the Navy, under the persistent goading of then-Captain Hyman Rickover, gradually warmed to the idea of nuclear submarines. Air Secretary Thomas K. Finletter seized the initiative and offered to provide Teller with a new laboratory under Air Force auspices. At this juncture the AEC ended the maneuvering by yielding to Teller's request and by providing separate facilities at Livermore, California.

Having thus acquired support, Teller and his co-workers settled down to the job. Theoretical ingenuity, especially on the part of Teller and mathematician Stanislaus Ulam, enabled a major advance, and a series of tests produced new data and confirmation of the theory. By June, 1951 Teller was able to present a revised theoretical design of an H-bomb to a two-day meeting of leading scientists and government officials at Princeton. The participants agreed that with these new developments the bomb was clearly feasible. Oppenheimer said later that, although it would not be meaningful to speculate upon what might have been the attitude of the GAC if this design had been available earlier, nevertheless "when you see something that is technically sweet, you go ahead and do it and you argue about it only after you have had your technical success." For this reason, he added, "I cannot well imagine if we had known in late 1949 what we got to know by early 1951 that the tone of our report would have been the same." [12]

While some scientists worked to develop the H-bomb, others who opposed it and what it represented in strategic terms, applied themselves to the study of military alternatives to an offensive strategy centered on this ultimate weapon. Project East River, under the direction of Otto L. Nelson Jr., with the active participation of Lloyd V. Berkner, inquired into the practical possibilities of civil defense on behalf of the National Security Resources Board. Lee DuBridge was put in charge of Project Vista, which was sponsored jointly by all three Services but guided by the Army. The Project was established to study problems of localized conflict relevant to the defense of Europe. Project Lincoln was set up under Air Force auspices to study problems of continental air defense.

Vista and Lincoln produced reports which caused consternation among those in the Air Force who were firmly attached to the policy of massive retaliation through the strategic use of nuclear weapons. The Vista report urged that Western Europe would best be defended by a readiness to use tactical atomic weapons in localized conflicts. A Lincoln summer study suggested that continental air defense was not only feasible but was a matter of high priority, since East River had concluded that without a system of warning and interception there could be no civil defense worth mentioning.

Because these proposals seemed to suggest alternatives to massive retaliation, they were subjected to criticism from the Air Force, including a campaign to discredit them as "Maginot Line" theories. In 1953 *Fortune* magazine published an article widely believed to have been inspired by elements in the Air Force, attacking the scientists active in the Lincoln summer study and Vista. It was even alleged that a cabal of four scientists (identified by their initials as "ZORC"—Jerrold Zacharias, Oppenheimer, Rabi, and Charles Lauritsen—from a telltale blackboard inscription) had masterminded a conspiratorial plot to subvert the Strategic Air Command.

Fanciful as such an accusation certainly was, it reflected a real conflict in which certain scientists had indeed sought to explore alternatives to a military policy that many of them found

[12] Testimony of J. Robert Oppenheimer, *Oppenheimer Transcript*, p. 81.

disagreeable and dangerous. At the basis of the accusation laid against the scientists by their military antagonists, and important to the proceedings which were to be initiated under political auspices to deprive Oppenheimer of his security clearance, was the recognition that scientists had for the first time asserted themselves not merely as neutral handmaidens of prevalent doctrine but as proponents of specific policy alternatives within the executive.

A Pattern of Responsibility

As the scientists renewed their direct contact with the military application of science it became apparent that they were guided by different attitudes. Hardest to characterize are those who gave no sign of political concern, who would work on military projects if the research was of interest to them but who raised no questions about the uses of their labor. Either they were politically indifferent or they believed that in a democracy no group of specialists has the right to exercise special authority or initiative in areas outside its area of technical competence. Although perhaps the most numerous, this group is of course the most difficult to identify; its members are given to passive acquiescence rather than to any form of activity or choice that might call attention to them.

Otherwise, scientists tended to take positions along a fairly well-defined spectrum. The spectrum extended from a militant advocacy of preparedness, reaching an extreme (to which few if any scientists would have subscribed) in the doctrine of preventive war, all the way to the uncompromising pacifism of those who recoiled in horror from all involvement with weapons technology (in some cases even with purely defensive efforts on the grounds that these presupposed or invited war) and were beginning to urge unilateral disarmament.

In between were scientists with sympathies in either direction, some leaning toward offensive strength and ultimate deterrents, others toward strategies emphasizing defensive strength, readiness for limited war and a willingness to negotiate settlements. Those in the first group tended to be concerned with weapons suitable to a strategy of massive retaliation. Those in the second sought to develop tactical weapons, systems of defense, and proposals for negotiation which might provide alternatives. In retrospect the work of both groups may well be said to have been complementary. Comprehensive military planning no doubt requires attention not only to ultimate deterrents, but also to capacity for small-scale conflict and defense. At the time, however, it appeared otherwise. Scientists in the first group accused those in the second of disloyalty, naïveté, and defeatism. Those in the second accused the others in turn of irresponsible servility and of an obsolete attachment to the notion that the greater the military power, the safer the society.

The mood of the nation lent support to the first group and rendered those in the second suspect. The attitude within the government invited the advice of the first group and excluded the others. In 1953, in a move that dramatized the political isolation of the excluded, Oppenheimer issued a call for what he termed "candor" with respect to our atomic weapons program.[13] It was in effect an indication that he and those for whom he spoke were no longer being given a hearing within the government. The call for candor was an appeal beyond the government to public opinion. The difficulty with this appeal, however, from the point of view of those who made it, was that its cause was unpopular and, furthermore, that in the absence of governmental sanction and political support, anyone identified with it quickly became highly vulnerable not only to criticism but to smear.

[13] J. Robert Oppenheimer, "Atomic Weapons and American Foreign Policy," *Foreign Affairs,* Vol. 31, No. 4 (July 1953), pp. 525-535.

7

SECURITY IN SCIENCE

Due to an uncongenial shift in the political climate, the scientists for whom Oppenheimer spoke found themselves in a precarious position. Many of those who had been most active as lobbyists and advisers lost influence when New Deal-Fair Deal policies and personalities gave way to a Republican administration in 1953. Public opinion had also undergone a less tangible but still perceptible shift against them. Among extremists, now growing in influence, it was the fashion to construe as communist or pro-communist any advocacy of active government intervention in domestic affairs or of international accommodation. Scientists associated with these positions were classed among the "eggheads" who were subjected to attack by the forces demanding vigilance at home and militance abroad. They also fell under a special accusation, unspoken but nonetheless felt, of having deliberately avoided scientific progress in weapons while their Russian counterparts had kept busy and left "peace propaganda" to the politicians.

Relegated by these circumstances to a kind of political limbo, scientists critical of official policy rapidly became vulnerable targets in the campaign for security and against "subversion," that agitated the nation from the end of the war until the censure of Senator Joseph McCarthy of Wisconsin. The problem of security in science had been growing in importance and complexity for some time, reaching a peak of intensity during the first years of the Eisenhower administration. If the effort made during these years had any clearly salutary effect it was in illuminating the special character of the real problem.

The Wartime Measures

As Lloyd V. Berkner has pointed out,[1] security and science first came together in modern times around 1930 when the discovery of radar was wrapped in a blanket of military secrecy. As a result of secrecy the technical development of radar suffered from neglect until the outbreak of war gave it urgent priority. Secrecy was also partly to blame for the failure of the Armed Forces to redesign their defensive procedures so as to take the fullest possible advantage of this new technique of detection. Pearl Harbor, Berkner observes, might have been much less costly if the services had been taught to make serious use of radar and to pay careful attention to the warnings it provided. Indeed, as he also suggests, had we made radar public the Japanese might never even have dared to attempt a surprise attack.

However controversial the wisdom of secrecy in science, no prominent scientist questioned it in principle during the War. Atomic scientists had imposed self-censorship even before official steps were taken. Security measures implemented by military specialists were accepted, not without some friction and criticism, but on the whole, by all accounts, with careful cooperation.

The security officers, more accustomed to the traditional difficulties involved in guarding confidential documents and military information, found science a fresh problem. They soon realized that scientific research could be hampered and rendered fruitless by overprotection. Nor were they used to dealing with scientists, who, unlike soldiers and even civil servants, had virtually no training in military or administrative discipline and even less inclination to seek any. As intellectuals, scientists were perhaps less likely than others to spy for material rewards, but might they not be more likely to spy out of political conviction? Yet how was anyone to judge the nature and extent of such conviction? The scientists were interested in all manner of extraordinary ideas. A number of them were foreigners; most of them were cosmopolitan and "inter-

[1] Lloyd V. Berkner, "Is Secrecy Effective?" *BAS*, Vol. X, No. 2 (February 1953), pp. 62-63, 68.

nationalist" in one way or another. Worse yet, how could a mere security officer tell scientists what should be kept secret and what not?

Throughout the War adjustments were made from both sides. Scientists obliged the security officers, for example, by traveling circuitous routes on trips about which family and friends were deliberately misled; foreign-born scientists dutifully used their fake names, even though some of them could scarcely pronounce the Anglo-Saxon sounds. The general categories of classification (restricted, confidential, secret, and top secret) were imposed on scientific documents considered of military value. In the Manhattan District secrecy was reinforced by compartmentalization, limiting a scientist to information for which he had what was called "a need to know." Many scientists were later to argue from the wartime experience that classification and compartmentalization cost more in scientific progress than they were worth as insurance against the disclosure of what was already known. This was an argument, however, with more force in peacetime than in war, especially since the war work was often of the kind about which it was essential to keep the enemy completely ignorant.

For their part the security officers were under constraint to manage personnel security with as much tact and deference as they could afford. The government considered it more important to the safety of the nation that the talents of scientists be fully exploited than that everyone who might not be fully trustworthy be removed from the work. It was therefore the policy of the security agencies to take a calculated risk, especially in cases involving scientists suspected of sympathy for the U.S.S.R., which was then a wartime ally.

These mutual adjustments worked brilliantly for the duration of the War. In part, it may well be that the work on the bomb succeeded so well and so rapidly because scientists were not inhibited from doing truly creative work and because they were treated with enough respect to make them fully conscious of their responsibilities. Nor was this confidence betrayed. So far as is known, no American scientist, citizen or resident, employed in the Manhattan Project committed a significant breach of security during the entire War.

Security and the Cold War: Congress

If the conduct of the scientists could arouse no serious complaint from the operating security agencies during the War, it did arouse suspicion after the War within Congress. One of the first inquiries of the revived House Committee on Un-American Activities was directed at "atomic espionage." In the lexicon of the Committee this term referred chiefly to cases where security agencies had collected information casting doubt on scientists who could not be successfully accused of any specific punishable violation of security.

An early and prominent target of the Committee was Edward U. Condon, then Director of the Bureau of Standards. Condon had made valuable contributions to the development of the proximity fuse as well as to the Manhattan Project. While on the Project he had all but openly defied the requirements of compartmentalization on grounds that the work could not proceed otherwise. His uncooperative attitude had aroused the anger of the security officers and of General Groves.[2] After the War he was among those who stood against military control of atomic energy. Among the supporters of the legislation defeated in this campaign was Representative J. Parnell Thomas of New Jersey, who later became Chairman of the Un-American Activities Committee.

On March 1, 1948, an Un-American Activities Subcommittee released a report describing Condon as "one of the weakest links" in atomic security. The remainder of the report is equally representative of the reckless sensationalism for which this Committee became notorious. Condon's wife, the Subcommittee notes, is of Czechoslovakian descent, a fact introduced solely in order to associate Condon (at whatever remove) with the Communist coup that had recently occurred in that country. Although cleared once before the report was made, Condon was investigated and cleared several times after the Subcommittee called attention to him. After enduring seven years of harassment Condon left government employ as well as a job as a consultant for a manufacturer holding a

[2] Testimony of John R. Lansdale, *Oppenheimer Transcript*, pp. 166, 173.

government contract. He was offered a post as chairman of the Physics Department of a large university, but the Chancellor told him that according to a trustee of the university, the university would lose federal support if he accepted.[3]

In the same month that the attack on Condon was begun, the Subcommittee also reported on "Soviet espionage activities" allegedly engaged in by a number of other scientists. Clarence Hiskey, a chemist, had been transferred from Los Alamos to the Army in 1943, when the security officers discovered that he had an inactive commission and took the opportunity to remove him from his post. Hiskey was accused by a fellow chemist, John H. Chapin, of having put him in contact with a Soviet espionage agent. Hiskey refused to testify on grounds of possible self-incrimination. Martin D. Kamen, also a chemist, was reported to have discussed classified activities with Soviet consular authorities at a San Francisco restaurant. Kamen conceded he had committed an indiscretion and the Subcommittee noted there was no evidence the revelations were "willful and deliberate." Joseph W. Weinberg, Giovanni R. Lomanitz, David J. Bohm, Max B. Friedman and Irving D. Fox, all scientists connected with the Radiation Laboratory at Berkeley, were accused of membership in a Communist cell at Berkeley which allegedly passed on secret information, but the hearings produced no evidence of any actual espionage.[4]

In 1949 the Joint Committee on Atomic Energy heard that an AEC fellowship had gone to a pro-communist graduate student and that the AEC conducted no screening of applicants. The AEC protested that the graduate student could have no access to classified information. But this did not satisfy Congressional critics. There is always the chance, Senator William Knowland of California objected, that some student, even if engaged in nonsecret studies, might "hit upon a 'superduper' atom bomb, and be off to Russia." [5]

[3] See Louis Wellborn, "The Ordeal of Dr. Condon," *Harper's Magazine* (January 1950), pp. 46-53; and Edward U. Condon, "Time to Stop Baiting Scientists," *BAS*, Vol. XIV, No. 2 (February 1958), pp. 80-82.

[4] See House Committee on Un-American Activities, *Report on Soviet Espionage Activities In Connection With the Atom Bomb*, 80th Cong., 2nd sess. (Washington, D.C.: Government Printing Office, 1948).

[5] Quoted in Walter Gellhorn, *Security, Loyalty and Science* (Ithaca: Cornell University Press, 1950), p. 198, from the 1949 JCAE Hearings on the AEC fellowship program.

The AEC agreed to require a loyalty oath and a non-communist affidavit, but on the insistence of certain Congressmen, a proviso that fellowship awards also require security clearance was attached as a rider to an appropriation. A year later, in a sequel played off-stage, the NSF fellowships were set up with a requirement of only an oath and an affidavit, whereupon the AEC quietly transferred its fellowship program to the NSF. In 1949 another brief flare-up over atomic secrecy was occasioned by Senator Hickenlooper's revelation that a millicurie of iron isotope had been sent by the AEC to Norway for nonmilitary research. So intense was the climate of suspicion that even this innocent gesture in support of basic science in a friendly country could attract vigilance.

Congressional pressure continued strong until perhaps 1954 when there were signs of change. It came to light that even the Department of Health, Education and Welfare was withholding fellowship funds pending loyalty checks. At the request of the White House, the president of the National Academy of Sciences, Detlev Bronk, appointed a committee to consider this practice. The committee condemned it sharply.

> The idea persists that the government in granting funds for research confers a favor upon scientists as individuals. We consider this contrary to the fact. In appropriating funds for the support of research, we believe the Congress to have been motivated by an urgent national need. . . . A fundamental contribution leading ultimately to the cure of cancer, providing it were made generally available, would be no less beneficial to all humanity for having been made by a Communist. Authentic scientific progress carries with it no ideological flavor from its source.[6]

The position of the NAS committee was accepted by the Department and no further criticism was heard from Congress.

The Executive Follows Suit

Pressures from Congress and the Cold War soon combined to induce the executive again to increase its concern with security in

[6] Quoted in Ralph S. Brown, *Loyalty and Security* (New Haven: Yale University Press, 1958), p. 69.

science. The Republicans had won an unprecedented victory in the off-year Congressional elections of 1946, and threatened to ride the Democrats out of the White House on the charge that the Truman administration had been lax in removing subversives from the government payroll. Abroad, the wartime amity between the Western powers and their Soviet ally had dissolved in the struggle for control over continental Europe. Faced with difficulties at home and abroad, the executive resolved to remove the initiative in security matters from Congress. On March 27, 1947, Executive Order 9835 established the Employees Loyalty Program. Together with a security law passed by Congress in 1950 enabling heads of important departments to suspend summarily those found subversive, the Truman Executive Order provided the ground rules for the primary procedures of the security program. The original standard for dismissal under the Truman program was reasonable *evidence* of disloyalty, but by 1951 the unabated demand for stricter standards was met by the adoption of the less permissive criterion of reasonable *doubt* of loyalty. Proof of actual disloyalty was thus no longer necessary so long as suspicion was strong. In political terms, this modification proved to be without dividends. The Republicans won in 1952, and, shortly after taking office, President Eisenhower redeemed a campaign pledge by issuing Executive Order 10450. By the terms of this new directive, it became permissible to discharge anyone whose employ could be considered not "consistent with the national security." The term "security risk" was made so broad that even someone whose loyalty was above suspicion might be fired. The Eisenhower order went beyond the Truman program in the direction of greater and more extensive emphasis on security.

The AEC meanwhile pruned its own ranks of doubtful employees in a separate security program set up in the Atomic Energy Act of 1946. The Commission had the responsibility of classifying secret information and clearing personnel involved in atomic work. The AEC program is chiefly distinguished from other federal security checks in that it permits applicants and employees alike the opportunity to request a review, a privilege available in other areas of the government service only to employees. In cooperation with the Department of Defense the AEC extended its procedures to include those employed by companies under contract to the government. By 1955 the AEC had investigated 504,000 people, denying clearance to 494 under all phases of its operations.[7]

McCarthy and the Signal Corps Scientists

A much publicized inquiry into scientific security was conducted by Senator McCarthy at the Army Signal Corps laboratories at Fort Monmouth, New Jersey. From August, 1953, to April, 1954, work at the labs was disrupted and public attention diverted by the sensational conduct of this inquiry. In October, 1953, McCarthy announced that the place "had all the earmarks of dangerous espionage." If so, it would have been a serious matter, for these labs were the nerve center of the effort of electronics engineers to develop defenses against air attack by improving radar and designing guidance systems for anti-missile missiles. The labs operated under a $75 million budget and employed 1,300 scientists and engineers. As a result of McCarthy's agitation, the Army suspended 48 employees. Charges against those suspended ranged from advocacy of foreign aid through subscriptions to liberal weeklies to membership in left-wing organizations over a period extending well back into the thirties. Within a year half of the 48 were fully reinstated, 8 were dismissed, and 12 were working without clearance. A committee of scientists appointed to examine the charges concluded that no evidence whatever had been presented to support a charge of espionage. Where foreign enemies had failed, McCarthyism availed: the work of the laboratory was seriously impaired. A quarter of the top personnel (rank GS 11 and above) was removed from one of the labs during the investigation and in other instances key personnel were removed from sensitive posts, only to be reinstated later. Six of those dismissed were later reinstated in 1958 by order of the U. S. Court of Appeals for the District of Columbia which found that the Army had violated its own regulations in firing them.[8]

[7] Ralph S. Brown, *Loyalty and Security*, p. 63.

[8] Murray Marder, "The Fort Monmouth Story," *BAS*, Vol. X, No. 1 (January 1954), pp. 19, 21-25; Scientists' Committee on Loyalty and Security, "Fort Monmouth One Year Later," *BAS*, Vol. XI, No. 9 (November 1955), p. 150; News Roundup prepared by Helen C. Allison, *BAS*, Vol. XIV, No. 7 (September 1958), p. 279.

The Espionage Cases

Although McCarthy never turned up any of the real thing, espionage involving foreign scientists and American citizens was uncovered shortly after the War. In 1945, when Igor Gouzenko, a clerk in the Soviet Embassy in Ottawa, made his dramatic defection, neither the executive nor the legislature was as yet preoccupied with security. Yet this one defection led to a discovery of actual espionage completely undetected by the costly and elaborate methods of security adopted by the government. From Gouzenko it was learned that the Soviet Union had been kept abreast of our progress in developing the atomic bomb, especially in regard to certain of the processes through which it was developed. When President Truman told Stalin at Potsdam of our success in exploding a new weapon in the Almagordo test and of our intention to use it against Japan, he had been surprised that Stalin took the news nonchalantly and did not press for details. Truman interpreted this bland reaction as evidence that Stalin did not yet comprehend the full significance of the new weapon. In view of what came out of the espionage investigations it seems more likely that Stalin knew quite well what was involved but did not wish to put us on our guard.

The two leading scientists implicated in the espionage ring were both British subjects, one a native and the other a naturalized German refugee. Alan Nunn May and Klaus Fuchs belonged to a generation which came to maturity in the years when the main issue of politics, domestic and international, seemed to be the conflict between the haves and the have-nots. Nunn May grew up in the English left, aroused by the desperate straits of the working class in the Depression and by the struggle against fascism in Spain. He seems not to have joined the Communist Party, however, either before or after he undertook military research. In 1940 he signed the Official Secrets Act, thereby promising not to divulge the nature or results of his work to unauthorized persons. Some time before 1944 Nunn May made initial contact with Soviet agents. He supplied them with information through 1945, also contriving to pass samples of uranium isotope (U-233).

When at length he was apprehended, Nunn May stated that his

decision to betray his country had not been taken lightly or for material gain. "I gave and had given very careful consideration," he said, "to correctness of making sure that development of atomic energy was not confined to USA. I took the very painful decision that it was necessary to convey general information on atomic energy and make sure it was taken seriously." It was, he added, "a contribution I could make to the safety of mankind." [9]

Apparently Nunn May had also concluded that it was within his right to decide to convey secret information outside ordinary channels in accordance with his personal political judgment. Apparently, too, he did not consider himself under any very great obligation to observe either his oath or the code of the civil service or the principles of representative government. Even more than the damage caused by his treason, what disturbed his English trial judge was the blow Nunn May had struck at the traditional foundations of all free government, the ability of government to rely on promises of its citizens and the willingness of citizens to regard the government as a fiduciary instrument. At the same time it was also a blow to the argument of scientists that men of their standing did not need to be submitted to the petty indignities of security checks.

Fuchs was in a higher position than Nunn May and therefore able to do more damage with a similar point of view. Born and raised in Germany, Fuchs passed from his father's Quaker pacifism through Social Democracy until finally, in the face of the Nazi rise to power over the ineffectual opposition of the republican parties, he became a Young Communist. Communism appealed to him on theoretical and practical grounds. "The idea which gripped me most," he explained later,

was the belief that in the past man has been unable to understand his own history and the forces which lead to the further development of human society; that now, for the first time, man understands the historical forces and he is able to control them, and that therefore for the first time he will be really free. I carried this idea over to the personal sphere and believed that I could understand myself and that I could make myself into what I would be.[10]

[9] Quoted in Joint Committee on Atomic Energy, *Soviet Atomic Espionage* (Washington, D.C.: Government Printing Office, 1951), pp. 58-59.
[10] Quoted by Alan. Moorehead, *The Traitors: The Double Life of Fuchs, Pontecorvo and Nunn May* (London: Hamish Hamilton, Ltd. 1952), p. 43.

Was it a further elaboration of this central understanding that led Fuchs to attempt to turn the tide of history by himself, or perhaps, as he might have understood it, to offer the achievements of his science to the uses of the society he regarded as the vanguard of emancipation? Whatever the reason, he was not long in arriving at it. Soon after having been interned in Canada as an alien upon the outbreak of war, Fuchs supplied the first of many reports to the Russians. At the outset these reports were limited to his own work. Later they extended to whatever work he had knowledge of. In 1943 Fuchs travelled to the U.S. to work on the effort to develop theoretically a method of producing U-235 from U-238 by the process of gaseous diffusion. The Russians were informed of all progress. In November, 1944, Fuchs passed information to Harry Gold, the American chemist who acted as an intermediary. In Los Alamos early in 1945 he passed to Gold details of the bomb which were supplemented with drawings depicting the implosion lens to be used as a firing mechanism. The drawings had been provided by David Greenglass, an Army sergeant working as a technician at Los Alamos.

Fuchs was not arrested until 1949. By then he had become the third-ranked scientist at Harwell, the British counterpart of Los Alamos. He confessed under sharp questioning, explaining that he had maintained a "controlled schizophrenia" enabling him to keep his associations at Harwell and at Los Alamos and at the same time to find independence from the surrounding forces of society by providing information to the Russians.[11]

An American industrial chemist, Alfred Dean Slack, was also implicated by Gold's testimony as a party to espionage in another area of research and development. Slack, who was employed at the Holston Ordnance Works in Tennessee, was convicted of giving Gold samples of a new explosive, RDX, which was developed there.

Security in Science: Cause and Effect

The problem of security in science is of such a peculiar nature, and the efforts made to achieve it so diverse, that it is difficult to

[11] Alan Moorehead, *The Traitors,* pp. 119-120.

make a sweeping assessment of the costs and benefits that have resulted. In themselves the investigations of the House Committee on Un-American Activities contributed little, if anything, of benefit and much that was harmful. They did indeed indirectly stimulate the executive to act more vigorously. It may be that the federal programs kept potential traitors who might have done great harm away from vital scientific work. The two scientist-spies were the responsibility of the British security system, not our own. It is certainly the case that grave injustices were inflicted by the American program on particular individuals, who were compelled to prove their innocence of charges that were frequently tenuous and irrelevant.

Injustice apart, the program is still open to serious question. Is the activity of the security probers deployed so widely that inadequate attention is paid to the really sensitive positions? A wry scientist has remarked in criticism of the federal program that "the moment we start guarding our toothbrushes and our diamond rings with equal zeal, we usually lose fewer toothbrushes but more diamond rings." [12]

The most important criticism may have been, however, that our absorption with secrets and spies has led us to think of security in science almost wholly as a job of guarding what we know from unreliable people. How important was the treason of Fuchs and Nunn May? How much did it actually help the Soviet Union? For years, scientists have been trying to explain that as a matter of fact science has no secrets in the ordinary sense. The most important secret of the atomic bomb, they have pointed out, was the knowledge that it could be made to work. Once that was known, it was only a matter of time before any technologically advanced nation could, if it wished, develop bombs of its own. In 1945 James G. Beckerley, former director of classification for the AEC, said, following the Soviet thermonuclear test: "It is time to stop 'kidding' ourselves about atomic 'secrets,' and time to stop believing that Soviet scientists are incompetent. . . . The atom bomb and the hydrogen bomb

[12] Ascribed to Prof. J. H. Van Vleck of Harvard by McGeorge Bundy in 1955 hearings of the Senate Committee on Government Operations, cited in Ralph S. Brown, *Loyalty and Security*, p. 253.

were not stolen from us by spies. . . . Espionage played a minor role in the attainment of successful weapons by the Soviets. . . ." [13] Ralph Lapp, the physicist, has noted that "the critical factor in determining when our own A-project paid off was not a weapons problem but a production problem." [14] The information they obtained through espionage no doubt saved the Russians money and time because it indicated what processes were sure to work, but it did not give them the scientific personnel, the resources and facilities, and the will to produce the bomb.

Many scientists have contended that because it is virtually impossible to keep scientific secrets for very long, it would pay us to release more of them for the sake of our own scientific progress. Secrecy, it has been argued, stifles the free exchange of ideas through which such progress is made. Loyalty and security checks, if they are to be effective, must take valuable time and set up barriers between the cleared and the uncleared which add further impediments. Classification is costly because it tends to promote duplication and delays and because it tends to keep new ideas from the younger men who would be most likely to develop them further. Ordinary textbooks are in some cases said to be ten to fifteen years behind the times because of classification. Scientists who teach advanced courses and do their thinking on advanced projects have sometimes found it necessary to refuse to answer the questions of their graduate students. The morale of scientists is also adversely affected when their foreign colleagues are prevented from entering the country for scientific conferences because of security policy. The refusal of visas to Nobel Prize physicists and chemists from England and France provided glaring examples of a general policy which has rankled and embarrassed many American scientists. Even some American scientists—the biochemist Linus Pauling is a prime example—have had difficulty in obtaining passports to make trips abroad. And international scientific conferences which had previously been convened in the United States found the U.S.S.R. anxious to offer hospitality.

Is there no better set of alternatives? Louis Ridenour has sug-

[13] Quoted by Lloyd V. Berkner, "Is Secrecy Effective?" *BAS*, Vol. X, No. 2 (February 1953), p. 68.
[14] Ralph E. Lapp, *The New Force*, p. 214.

gested that far more desirable than a security of concealment and exclusion is a security of achievement.[15] The argument that scientific achievement is too important to sacrifice for the sake of air-tight security is one that has grown in persuasiveness with every new development in the international competition between ourselves and the Communists. Scientific secrets depreciate at a very high rate in a very short time. It may well be that secrecy is effective only in keeping our own scientists in doubt. "When we lock the laboratory door," C. F. Kettering said, "we keep out more than we keep in." [16] Would it not make more sense, in other words, to concentrate on advancing our science rather than on trying in vain to sit on what we have; to build a positive security rather than rely on negative security?

Security and Insecurity

Many of the security concerns of the postwar period no doubt must be judged less as rational efforts to safeguard the country than as irrational expressions of anxiety. This anxiety found expression most easily in Congress, partly because anti-Communism was a convenient ladder for the ambitious, partly also because the investigative function seemed to many the only real means remaining to the legislative branch for effective participation in important decision-making, in the face of the steady expansion of Presidential power.

That scientists became the object of anxiety stemmed in part from their decision to risk their dignified apolitical image by taking partisan positions. But it was in part also because they chose methods of political involvement that effectively alienated many in the executive, civilian and military alike, and that did not enable them to develop the kind of ties with Congress that other professional and special-interest groups cultivate as their first order of business.

The relations of the scientists to Congress indicate at the same time something perhaps even more fundamental. Why, after all, were these relations almost exclusively concerned with security

[15] Louis Ridenour, "Secrecy in Science," *BAS*, Vol. I, No. 6 (March 1946), pp. 3, 8.
[16] Quoted *ibid.*, p. 3.

and not with science and its social and political implications? It would seem that the public and its legislative representatives simply had very little understanding of the role of the scientist in society and politics, and even less appreciation for the problems the scientists were trying to call to their attention. Only two years after the War ended, some of our public figures seemed confused about the role of scientists in the wartime accomplishments. Senator McKellar, the bitter foe of David Lilienthal since TVA days, delivered the following tirade in the hearings to consider confirming Lilienthal's appointment as chairman of the AEC:

> So you are willing to admit, are you, that this secret, or the first history of it, dated from the time when Alexander the Great had his Macedonian scientists trying to make this discovery, and then Lucretius wrote a poem about it, about 2,000 years ago?
>
> And everybody has been trying to discover it, or most scientists have been trying to discover it ever since. And do you not really think that General Groves, for having discovered it, is entitled to some little credit for it? Is that your position?

When Lilienthal responded that General Groves deserved a great deal of credit for his direction of the Manhattan Project, Senator McKellar pressed on:

> Did it not seem remarkable to you, who have never even been an engineer, who knew nothing in the world about the splitting of the atom or about atomic energy and its discovery, that the President should not reappoint General Groves, who was an engineer, and who had made this greatest discovery of all time? [17]

When it was testified that Karl T. Compton, Enrico Fermi, Harold Urey, and James B. Conant were strongly in favor of Lilienthal's appointment on the ground that he would advance the development of atomic energy, Senator Styles Bridges' reaction was, "pure undiluted bunk." His colleague, Senator Brewster of Maine, said that he

[17] *Confirmation of Atomic Energy Commission and General Manager, Hearings Before the Senate Section of the Joint Committee on Atomic Energy,* January 27-March 14, 1947 (Washington, D.C.: Government Printing Office, 1947), p. 20.

thought the twenties had been the time when government had to
protect itself against big business, the thirties and the present
against big labor, and the immediate future against big science.
Senator Brewster also unburdened himself of this classic specimen
of Capitolese:

> And I say to my friends in science that greatly as we appreciate
> their achievement, profoundly as we respect their knowledge, they do
> not have a monopoly on the political wisdom that is essential to the
> solution of the problem we here face; and with all deference we say
> to them that if they will show a little more deference to the Congress
> of the United States, as possibly having an equal patriotic devotion
> to the common good, and perhaps a little understanding of all the
> political aspects, and that perhaps is a subject to which some of us
> have devoted our time and talents, and if there will be a little recog-
> nition on their part of our knowledge regarding some aspects of the
> conduct of governmental business with which they have not been
> hitherto concerned, it would be a salutary lesson to the people of
> the United States.

To all of which Senator Bridges responded: "I want to congratulate
the Senator from Maine. To me it is a terrible thing that scientists
should infer [sic] that they are going on a strike against America
simply because the government does not do what they want done." [18]

These were early and unusual statements but they indicate the
tenor of permissible opinion and they provide a logical preview of
what was to come in the loyalty-security campaign. The Congressional power of investigation became a vehicle for a variety of re-
sentments: against the executive for displacing the legislative,
especially in foreign policy, and against the experts for paying insufficient deference to the popular will. The heart of the trouble,
Edward A. Shils has speculated, was that the scientists, like other
professionals, were the victims of a populist uprising against expertise, a democratic tradition dating back to the age of Jackson
and newly stimulated by the frustrations of the Cold War. Among
experts the scientists were peculiarly vulnerable.[19] They worked in

[18] Quoted in "The Senate Debates Mr. Lilienthal's Confirmation, March
24-April 9, 1947," *BAS*, Vol. III, No. 6, pp. 158-162, 168.

[19] Edward A. Shils, *The Torment of Secrecy* (Glencoe, Ill.: The Free Press,
1956).

some of the most sensitive areas of national security, and they were altogether without traditional associations with Congress and without any of the powerful public support on which the clergy, the military, the medical, and other professions could count.

If this interpretation has merit, it is certainly ironic that the scientists should have come to feel that their only recourse lay in an appeal for public support. The public and its politicians were never more distrustful of the scientists than they were in this period. The appeal fell on deaf ears and its principal author became the leading victim of the crusade. Oppenheimer was compelled to exercise his sense of political responsibility not in the lobbies of Congress or in the offices of the executive but in the silence of the interior monologue. If there was to be a public revelation of nuclear policy it was to come not from the leaders of state but from the hearing that Oppenheimer requested to consider the revocation of his security clearance. As Ralph Lapp put it, "the Oppenheimer transcript is Operation Candor." [20]

[20] Ralph Lapp, "Atomic Candor," *BAS*, Vol. X, No. 7 (September 1954), p. 336.

8

ALIENATION AND RESPONSIBILITY

The Trial of Dr. Oppenheimer

The revocation of Oppenheimer's security clearance by the Atomic Energy Commission was far more than another routine episode in the security program. Oppenheimer had earned the Medal of Merit and wide esteem for his brilliant performance as wartime Director of the Los Alamos Laboratory. Afterward he continued to gain recognition as perhaps the leading spokesman of scientists and as one of the most intelligent and articulate figures in American public life. Suddenly after a decade of prominent service to government, he was branded a security risk and barred from further access to classified data.

Even in the way it unfolded the case was unusual. On November 7, 1953, William L. Borden, who had been until shortly before executive director of the staff of the Joint Committee on Atomic Energy, addressed a letter to the director of the FBI, J. Edgar Hoover, casting the gravest aspersions upon Oppenheimer's loyalty and asserting that his importance in government posed a serious threat to national security. Borden had the audacity to say that after studying the evidence carefully it was his conclusion that "more probably than not J. Robert Oppenheimer is an agent of the Soviet Union." [1] Borden was led to this conclusion not because of any new information implicating Oppenheimer in espionage or in any breach of security but because Oppenheimer's opposition to the H-bomb crash program in 1950 (and afterward as well, he claimed,) seemed to confirm the suspicions raised by information long in the FBI dossier.

[1] Testimony of William L. Borden, *Oppenheimer Transcript*, p. 837.

Hoover referred the letter to the White House. President Eisenhower conferred with Admiral Lewis Strauss, whom he had appointed Chairman of the Atomic Energy Commission. Strauss afterward announced that the Atomic Energy Commission would review Oppenheimer's clearance in accordance with new regulations that had come into effect since the clearance had originally been provided. Pending the outcome of this review a "blank wall" was to be put between Oppenheimer and classified data. Reportedly members of the administration urged this course lest Senator Mc-Carthy seize the opportunity to stage another of his investigative spectaculars. It has been charged, however, by Joseph and Stewart Alsop, that Strauss was mainly instrumental in turning the whole affair into a vindictive punishment of Oppenheimer, who had opposed him on several occasions and made him appear foolish.[2]

Oppenheimer's request for a review was granted, but after a lengthy and detailed hearing the revocation was sustained by majority vote, first of a special three-member board and then of the full five-man Commission. Far from closing the case, however, publication of the transcript of the hearing "in the matter of J. Robert Oppenheimer" only provided fuel for a controversy which was to rage for several years. The inquiry shed a great deal of light not only over the case at hand but also over the entire record of relations between government and scientists, over the operation of the "security system," and over the development of national military policy.

Nor was the hearing lacking in the flavor of pungent personal and professional antagonism. A number of scientists hostile to Oppenheimer testified to his all but magical powers of persuasion. One eminent physicist swore that he was "one of the most persuasive men that has ever lived." [3] Another scientist testified that Oppenheimer was "one of the most amazing people that this country has ever produced in his ability to influence people." Young men, he said, were sent to Los Alamos politically innocent and came back pacifists—"due largely to his influence, this tremendous influence he had over these young men." Asked if he himself had fallen under

[2] Joseph and Stewart Alsop, *We Accuse! The Story of the Miscarriage of American Justice in the Case of J. Robert Oppenheimer* (New York: Simon & Schuster, 1954).

[3] Testimony of Luis W. Alvarez, *Oppenheimer Transcript,* p. 802.

Oppenheimer's influence he solemnly replied: "No. I don't believe I was in close enough contact to be. I might have been if I had been in close contact." [4]

Equally bizarre were certain of the remarks introduced into evidence by military officers. An Air Force general testified that his suspicions of Oppenheimer were aroused when the scientist opposed a proposal for nuclear-powered aircraft even though he supported one for nuclear-powered ships.[5] The wartime report of an Army security officer offered a revealing glimpse of the process of psychological projection by which the military sought to fathom the depths of "the scientific mind." Oppenheimer, it seemed, was to be understood as a man chiefly concerned with the contest for power and glory. "It is the opinion of this officer," he wrote,

> that Oppenheimer is deeply concerned with gaining a worldwide reputation as a scientist, and a place in history, as a result of the DSM project. It is also believed that the Army is in the position of being able to allow him to do so or to destroy his name, reputation, and career, if it should choose to do so. Such a possibility, if strongly presented to him, would possibly give him a different view of his position with respect to the Army, which has been, hitherto, one in which he has been dominant due to his supposed essentiality.[6]

No less questionable than some of the testimony was the conduct of the committee counsel, Roger Robb, who often chose to behave as though he were the prosecutor in an adversary proceeding. Of this behavior there is no more telling illustration than the manner in which he concluded his effort to discredit the testimony of Hans Bethe.

Q. Doctor, how many divisions were there at Los Alamos?
A. It changed somewhat in the course of time. As far as I could count the other day, there were 7, but there may have been 8 or 9 at some time.
Q. Which division was Klaus Fuchs in?
A. He was in my division which was the Theoretical Division.
Q. Thank you. That is all.[7]

[4] Testimony of Wendell M. Latimer, *Oppenheimer Transcript*, pp. 659-660, 663.
[5] Testimony of Gen. Roscoe Wilson, *Oppenheimer Transcript*, p. 684.
[6] Report of Capt. Peer de Silva, *Oppenheimer Transcript*, p. 275.
[7] *Oppenheimer Transcript*, p. 331.

But if the motives behind the reconsideration of Oppenheimer's clearance were mixed and the subjective element in the hearing unsettling, the opinions sustaining revocation were nothing short of confused. The Personnel Security Board, headed by Gordon Gray, ruled two to one that Oppenheimer was a security risk, in the broad sense of the Eisenhower directive, because he had shown "bad judgment" in opposing the crash program and in displaying a lack of enthusiasm toward it.[8] In this opinion Gray and Thomas A. Morgan followed the line of reasoning indicated by Edward Teller in the hearing. Asked whether in his opinion Oppenheimer was a security risk, Teller replied, reflecting on Oppenheimer's opposition to the crash program: "If it is a question of wisdom and judgment, as demonstrated by actions since 1945, then I would say one would be wiser not to grant clearance."[9] The chemist Ward V. Evans dissented, denying that Oppenheimer had in any way hindered the development of the H-bomb. "His judgment," Evans wrote, "was bad in some cases and most excellent in others but, in my estimation, it is better now than it was in 1947 and to damn him now and ruin his career and his service, I cannot do it."[10]

The decision of the Board was upheld by a four-to-one vote of the Commissioners, but on entirely different grounds. Oppenheimer's opposition to the crash program was now dismissed as entirely irrelevant. To do otherwise, the majority observed, might amount to punishing an adviser for expressing opinions not shared by those who asked his advice. Instead Oppenheimer was declared a security risk solely because "incidents in the record" led the Commissioners to conclude that he had exhibited "defects of character" and had entered into associations with unreliable people.[11] Thus, although his security clearance was originally brought into question and revocation first sustained because of the advice he had given, it was finally withdrawn on the basis of information which had previously been considered and discounted and which might never

[8] In the Matter of J. Robert Oppenheimer, Texts of Principal Documents and Letters of Personnel Security Board, General Manager, Commissioners, Washington, D.C., May 27, 1954 through June 29, 1954 (Washington, D.C.: Government Printing Office, 1954), p. 12. Hereafter referred to as Oppenheimer Texts.

[9] Testimony of Edward Teller, Oppenheimer Transcript, p. 726.

[10] Oppenheimer Texts, p. 22.

[11] Oppenheimer Texts, p. 51.

have been reconsidered had it not been for the advice Oppenheimer offered.

The charge of defects of character was put to Oppenheimer because he temporarily misled security officers in what came to be called "the Chevalier incident." While Oppenheimer was Director of Los Alamos, his friend Haakon Chevalier, a writer and then a teacher of Romance languages, proposed to him that information on the work of American scientists be sent to the Russians through a man at the Soviet consulate who had "experience with microfilm and that sort of thing." [12] According to his testimony, Oppenheimer immediately dismissed this suggestion on the ground that any such information could only be transmitted through official channels. Later, when asked by security officers whether there was anything of a suspicious nature that he could tell them about, Oppenheimer brought up the incident, but in a vague and inaccurate form. He said that he believed three people on the Manhattan Project had been approached with the proposal but he named only the man who he said had made the approach. After further questioning he indicated that the approach had been made to only one person, himself, through an intermediary whom he would designate only as "Professor X." From the start he said he would name the man if General Groves ordered him to do so. When General Groves did ask him, Oppenheimer finally named Chevalier, explaining that he had been reluctant to get his friend into trouble because in his judgment the man had been guilty of no more than an improper suggestion. The really dangerous man, he insisted, was the one he had named from the start, George Eltonton, who had inspired the suggestion and had offered to transmit the information.

When the Chevalier incident came up in the hearing, counsel Robb got Oppenheimer to agree that in it he had told the security officers a "tissue of lies" and even to volunteer that it was a "cock and bull story." [13] John Lansdale, Jr., who had been chief security officer for the atomic bomb project, put a rather different construction on it. He felt that Oppenheimer's reluctance to name Chevalier was typical of what security officers had to contend with in dealing with scientists.

---

[12] Testimony of J. Robert Oppenheimer, *Oppenheimer Transcript*, p. 875.
[13] *Oppenheimer Transcript*, pp. 149, 153.

The scientists en masse presented an extremely difficult problem. The reason for it, as near as I can judge, is that with certain outstanding exceptions they lack what I call breadth. They were extremely competent in their chosen field but their extreme competence in their chosen field lead [*sic*] them falsely to believe that there were as competent in any other field.

The result when you got them together was to make administration pretty difficult because each one thought that he could administer the administrative aspects of the Army post better than any Army officer, for example, and didn't hesitate to say so with respect to any detail of living or security or anything else.

Oppenheimer was not one of the exceptions, but neither was he especially difficult. On the contrary, Lansdale testified, he had been "extremely cooperative" in security matters.[14] It was Lansdale's judgment "on the basis of information I had then that Dr. Oppenheimer was loyal and discreet." [15] There is no small irony to the fact that despite Lansdale's testimony this one incident should have been used to impeach Oppenheimer for "defects of character." For in explaining to Lansdale at the time why he would not reveal the identity of "Professor X," Oppenheimer had told him: "What I want to say is this—I'm not kidding you and I'm not trying to weasel out. It's my overwhelming judgment that this guy isn't involved. That isn't judgment which is based on hope but his character." [16]

The Chevalier incident was the closest Oppenheimer came to being accused of having been involved in the betrayal of secrets. The remainder of the charges referred to Oppenheimer's intimacy before, during, and after the War with people who had been involved in left-wing causes, as he had been himself, during the thirties and early forties. Among these were his wife and his brother. He was also criticized for having paid a visit, while Director of the Los Alamos Laboratory, to a former fiancée whom he knew to have been a Communist. "You spent the night with her, didn't you?" asked counsel Robb. "Did you think that consistent with good security?" [17]

[14] Testimony of John Lansdale, Jr., *Oppenheimer Transcript,* p. 262.
[15] *Oppenheimer Transcript,* p. 267.
[16] Testimony of J. Robert Oppenheimer, *Oppenheimer Transcript,* p. 875.
[17] *Oppenheimer Transcript,* p. 154.

In no case was it alleged that Oppenheimer's relations with politically unreliable people went beyond personal intimacy or professional interest. Commissioner Thomas E. Murray insisted it made no difference.

> It will not do to plead that Dr. Oppenheimer revealed no secrets to the Communists and fellow travelers with whom he chose to associate. What is incompatible with obedience to security is the associations themselves, however innocent in fact.[18]

During the hearing George F. Kennan observed during his testimony that "people in senior positions in the government" should be "conceded maturity of judgment" enough to know when they should or should not associate with suspect people. He found it hard to accept the idea that such people should be required to forgo all such associations even though these in no way affected their performance of official functions. Exceptional people, he suggested, "are often apt not to fit into any categories of requirements that it is easy to write into an act or a series of loyalty regulations." [19] The Gray Board and Commission majorities were inclined to take a narrower view of the responsibility of public officials, whatever their rank or ability, to adhere to the rules restricting associations.

A similar strictness characterized the Gray Board majority opinion on the issue of the definition of the role of an adviser. The division among the scientists over military policy had become clear in the course of the hearing. The Gray Board opinion therefore addressed itself to the job of fashioning a standard for the limitation of the advisory role of scientists. But even in its own terms, the definition they offered was not so strict as they intended. If anything, it indicated the danger of drawing a strict definition. The standard ostensibly called for perfect self-restraint and neutrality on the part of technical advisers but in effect sanctioned the policy orientation of those partisan to "offensive strength." The reasoning of the majority opinion indicates the treacherous nature of the ground. First came the statement of the ideal standard:

[18] *Oppenheimer Tests*, p. 63.
[19] Testimony of George F. Kennan, *Oppenheimer Transcript*, pp. 368, 365.

It is vitally important that Government and scientists alike understand the need for and value of the advice of competent technicians. . . . Yet, those officials in Government who are responsible for the security of the country must be certain that the advice which they seriously seek appropriately reflects special competence on the one hand, and soundly based conviction on the other, uncolored and uninfluenced by considerations of an emotional character.

Then came the rather less objective application of the standard:

In evaluating advice from a specialist which departs from the area of his specialty, Government officials charged with the military posture of our country must also be certain that underlying any advice is a genuine conviction that this country cannot in the interest of security have less than the strongest possible offensive capabilities in time of war.[20]

Oppenheimer, the Gray-Morgan judgment contended, violated the standard. He had a right to his opinions, the statement admitted, but it nevertheless seemed "that he may have departed from his role as scientific adviser to exercise highly persuasive influence in matters in which his convictions were not necessarily a reflection of technical judgment, and also not necessarily related to the protection of the strongest possible military interests of this country." [21]

Clearly it is a dangerous and, to say the least, awkward, standard that makes it possible to indict an adviser as a security risk when his advice has defensive rather than offensive value.

If the disagreement in military policy among scientists interested the Gray Board for reasons pertaining to the role of the scientist as adviser, it interested the scientists themselves for reasons reaching beyond their social and political role to the very nature of their vocation. Teller testified that when the GAC's report advising against a crash program was made known to the scientists at Los Alamos, it was received with a sense of shock and disappointment.

First of all, people were interested in going on with the thermonuclear device because during the war it had been generally under-

[20] *Oppenheimer Texts*, p. 17.
[21] *Oppenheimer Texts*, pp. 18-19.

stood that this was one of the things that the laboratory was to find out at some time or other. It was a sort of promise in all of our minds.

Another thing was that the people there were a little bit tired— at least many, particularly of the younger ones—of going ahead with minor improvements and wanted to in sort of an adventurous spirit go into a new field.

However, I think the strongest point and the one which was a reaction to this report was this: Not only to me, but to very many others who said this to me spontaneously, the report meant this. As long as you people go ahead and make minor improvements and work very hard and diligently at it, you are doing a fine job, but if you succeed in making a really great piece of progress, then you are doing something immoral.[22]

The notion of science as an adventure in knowledge, to be pursued wherever it leads, regardless of the consequences, was by no means foreign to scientists other than those whose reactions were described by Teller. When the new concept of the bomb was outlined at Princeton in 1951, Teller testified, it was "warmly supported" by Oppenheimer. Teller recalled having been told at the time that Oppenheimer had said in effect "that if anything of this kind had been suggested right away he would never have opposed it." [23] Oppenheimer himself testified that his position and the GAC report might well have been different if something as "technically sweet" had been proposed earlier.[24]

The fact remains, however, that Oppenheimer—and the others on the GAC—opposed the crash program on grounds that were political and moral as well as technical. What finally seems to distinguish Oppenheimer from Teller is not so much a clear conflict of principle, but rather that Teller adhered consistently to the view that science must be pursued with no reservations, whereas Oppenheimer wavered. Oppenheimer may well have been reflecting on this dilemma in his concluding address to the Columbia Bicentennial Celebration:

When a friend tells of a new discovery, we may not be able to listen without jeopardizing the work that is ours and closer to us;

[22] Testimony of Edward Teller, *Oppenheimer Transcript,* p. 716.
[23] *Oppenheimer Transcript,* p. 714.
[24] Testimony of J. Robert Oppenheimer, *Oppenheimer Transcript,* p. 81.

but we cannot find in a book or canon—and we should not seek—grounds for hallowing our ignorance. If a man tells us that he sees differently, or that he finds beautiful what we find ugly, we may have to leave the room, from fatigue or trouble; but that is our weakness and our default.[25]

If this was in any sense a veiled concession to Teller, it was still not without ambiguity. For in the same address Oppenheimer seemed to be suggesting that creative artists and scientists not only "leave the room" but withdraw from the larger society, with its pandering politicians and mass media, to the "villages"—the universities and workshops—where they can pursue their callings faithfully and where alone they can achieve "true community." [26] If on the one hand Oppenheimer reaffirmed his belief in the untrammeled pursuit of knowledge, at the same time he seemed to express despair at what society did with that knowledge, and he seemed to counsel the creative minority to withdraw to a more congenial environment. The ambivalence of this position no doubt was a sign of the sense of frustration felt by Oppenheimer and others like him who had sought to play a responsible role in society but now felt themselves rejected and repudiated.

Fallout and Testing: The AEC and Its Critics

The trial of Dr. Oppenheimer marked and contributed to the most severe alienation of scientists in the postwar period. The ones hardest hit were those who had tried to fulfill their sense of responsibility by proposing and supporting military and political policies within the framework of the Cold War but on the side of limited war, defense, and negotiation, rather than on that of massive retaliation and ultimate deterrence. For a time only two real alternatives seemed to remain open: withdrawal, as had been suggested earlier and now, apparently by Oppenheimer; or complete unquestioning subservience to the policy of offensive strength in the form of ever more deadly weapons and ever more efficient systems of

[25] J. Robert Oppenheimer, "Prospects in the Arts and Sciences," *The Open Mind* (New York: Simon & Schuster, 1955), pp. 144-145. The speech was delivered in November, 1954.

[26] J. Robert Oppenheimer, "Prospects in the Arts and Sciences," *passim.*

delivery. Under the auspices of Secretary of State John Foster Dulles, massive retaliation was renamed "The New Look," and those scientists associated with this policy came into official favor.

Nevertheless, this one-sided situation did not last very long. Ironically it was the H-bomb itself, the production of which had so damaged the critics of massive retaliation, that now provided them with another set of opportunities. No one particular incident can be said to mark the turning point, but it certainly took place around one problem. In March, 1954 the AEC conducted in the Bikini atoll a test of a thermonuclear device which was to have important repercussions. Ralph Lapp, in *The Voyage of the Lucky Dragon*,[27] has told the story of the Japanese tuna boat showered with radioactive ash from the explosion over 200 miles away. Twenty-three of the crew were sickened. One died of his wounds soon afterward, and the others developed serious disabilities. As a result fear became widespread that the H-bomb had enormously increased the dangers from radioactivity, not only in the event of war, but even from testing.

Just how great was the danger proved a difficult question to answer. Even before the 1954 test, the AEC, at the prompting of Commissioner Willard Libby, set up what it called "Project Sunshine" to study the extent of radioactive contamination produced in thermonuclear explosions. The first report from the project was not available until almost a year after the Bikini test, or not until February, 1955. Meanwhile scientists not affiliated with the AEC study had begun to ask searching questions and to undertake experiments and calculations.

In the process many emerged from the relatively negative position of expressing disillusionment or anger at the security inquiries. Renewing active criticism, Einstein and Bertrand Russell joined in a request for a meeting of scientists to discuss ways of stopping the race to nuclear suicide. The Eisenhower administration sought to emphasize the peaceful application of atomic energy and joined the U.S.S.R. in promoting in August, 1955 a conference on atomic energy at Geneva, but both sides recognized that at most this conference would contribute to an easing of psychological tensions but

[27] Ralph Lapp, *The Voyage of the Lucky Dragon* (New York: Harper & Brothers, 1958).

not to important substantive agreement. The critical scientists could take little inspiration from it. Eugene Rabinowitch, the editor of the *Bulletin of Atomic Scientists,* lamented what he feared was the passing of the last opportunity to achieve control of nuclear weapons. From 1945 to 1949, while atomic stockpiles had been small, he argued, it might still have been possible. In 1955, however, any prospective signatory to a treaty had to be sure that other states were revealing the actual size of their stockpiles. Moreover, it had been found much easier than it had been thought at first to divert fissionable materials from industrial to military purposes. The years of atomic penury, Rabinowitch concluded, were past; the years of atomic plenty were upon us.[28]

What then remained feasible through political agitation? Throughout 1954 and 1955 the answer seemed to concern radioactive fallout. When the AEC issued its first findings they seemed to be reassuring. But even the publication of the report was in some respects suspicious. On February 11 the *Bulletin* published an analysis of the fallout problem by Ralph Lapp based on nonclassified information. On February 15 the AEC published a report of its own. Lapp's article had indicated that the tremendous increase of contamination caused by a thermonuclear explosion affected not only the immediate area of the blast but areas far removed to which the wind might carry contaminated particles. The explosion was also said to produce not only immediate but long-range danger because of the half-life of some of the radioactive particles, notably Strontium 90 and Cesium 137. Critics of the AEC wondered whether the Commission chose to call its study Project Sunshine in order to suggest that radioactivity was no more dangerous than ordinary sunshine. Nor were their suspicions laid to rest when Strauss announced warmly that the tests yielded information valuable "not only from a military point of view but from a humanitarian aspect." [29]

With these conflicting statements the battle lines were drawn anew. From then on, the scientists who had already expressed oppo-

---

[28] "Ten Years That Changed the World," *BAS,* Vol. XII, No. 1 (January 1956), p. 6.

[29] Quoted by Ralph Lapp, "The 'Humanitarian' H-Bomb," *BAS,* Vol. XII, No. 7 (September 1956), p. 263.

sition to the H-bomb, but who now felt that because of the new weapon disarmament was even less likely than before, now recognized in the threat of radioactive contamination an issue upon which they could make a fresh approach. If those who stood for a strategy of strength were pleased by the attainment of the H-bomb, those who sought alternatives to a policy of power gradually discovered that it could also be turned to their use.

The AEC report, it was charged, ignored the problem of how long fallout persists in the atmosphere. Some scientists calculated that some of the elements would remain there for weeks and months. The report did not clearly indicate that the extent of fallout produced was perhaps 300 times that of the Nagasaki bomb; that Strontium 90 would linger for 28 years; that the tests might produce undesirable genetic effects. By resorting to percentage figures, it was said, the AEC had avoided the need to admit bluntly that each test might cause 20,000 mutations, bringing disfigurement and death. In the February report the AEC suggested that 7,000 square miles might be dusted with fallout from a single test. Later the figure was revised by Libby to 100,000 square miles.

If these criticisms were not altogether ignored, it was because Congress at long last appeared to tire of its security fixation and to take a sober look not only at the military applications of atomic energy but also at the dangers those military applications entailed. Thoughtful Congressmen were also coming to understand that the alienation of the scientists was dangerous in itself and that many of their criticisms of security and military policy were at least sensible, even if their alternatives might be too radical. Only a week after the Oppenheimer hearing, a Subcommittee of the House Committee on Government Operations heard testimony on the Organization and Administration of the Military Research and Development Programs. They heard the eminent mathematician John von Neumann of Princeton urge them to clean up the security situation and to promote a climate which scientists would find receptive. James R. Killian, Jr. warned the Subcommittee that relations between scientists and government had deteriorated badly. Other scientists pointed out that military policy sometimes conflicted with, and needed to be adapted to, the needs of scientific research. They noted, for example, that just when an officer acquired a good understanding of a project and good working relations with scientific personnel, he would be transferred to an altogether different post because the services believed in rotation of officers but took no account of the special conditions of scientific supervision.

A subcommittee of the JCAE took up the criticisms of the scientists in hearings on fallout. Subcommittee Chairman Representative Chet Holifield of California indicated annoyance at the "huckstering" techniques used by the AEC to make people feel the bomb was really humanitarian. He learned from Civil Defense authorities that the AEC had not told them of the new scope of fallout, on the ground that it was classified information—even though it would have had significant interest for civil defense planners. The Subcommittee also reported that "the AEC displays a kind of easy optimism about nuclear explosive effects. The AEC spokesmen dwell upon the effects of 'nominal' (?) bombs rather than those of the high yield megaton weapons." The report further charged that the AEC used misleading averages of radiation hazards rather than figures which indicate that radiation was intense enough in certain areas to be dangerous. On the issue of genetic hazards, said the report, the AEC suggests only that there is a "wide range of admissible opinion on this subject," thereby sidestepping the issue raised by critics. Vital information, the Subcommittee also noted, only comes from the AEC in bits and pieces or in terms so abstruse and technical that they cannot readily be understood by the lay public.[30]

Such sharp criticism of the AEC, much of it no doubt inspired by scientists critical of prevailing policy, was a new experience for the Congress. Not since the days of the McMahon Act controversy, when the scientists had their highest prestige and even a letter-writing public behind them, had they found Congress so receptive. In part, Congressional interest was political and partisan. If the scientists were critics of the administration they were welcome in Congress—as they had not been when they were still high in the councils of the administration. They were especially welcome among Democrats anxious to hang something on the Republicans, and to those on the Joint Committee who, in the period of Strauss's chair-

[30] Draw from the summary of the report of the Subcommittee in Mary M. Simpson, "A Long Hard Look at Civil Defense, A Review of the Holifield Committee Hearings," *BAS*, Vol. XII, No. 9 (November 1956), p. 344.

manship of the AEC, found themselves more than ever cut off from decisions and information. Partly too, however, it was because of public concern over fallout, which became at times extremely exaggerated. A reporter discovered that ordinary white bread sold in a New York store had four times the amount that the AEC considered a maximum permissible limit of radioactive strontium. Scientists pointed out that radioactivity had a special affinity for the Northern hemisphere and that we therefore reap in Kansas what we sow in the Marshall Islands. Dairy farmers reported a panic among consumers who had been told that Strontium 90 had a great affinity for calcium transmitted in the milk of cows which grazed on land dusted with fallout from hydrogen bombs. The nation was startled to learn what General James M. Gavin had told a Senate Committee in executive session. An H-bomb attack on Russia, he had testified, could result "in several hundred million deaths," either in Russian areas and east to Japan, or in Western Europe— "depending," as he put it, "upon which way the wind blew." [31]

In response to mounting anxiety and criticism, the AEC enlisted the assistance of the National Academy of Sciences, a committee of which issued a report supporting Libby's contention that radioactivity from testing was an insignificantly small fraction of ordinary radiation. Skeptical scientists commented that the data used were old and inadequate. British scientists meanwhile chipped in new fuel in the form of independent studies with conclusions contradicting the AEC findings. In 1956 the AEC also received critical inquiries from Albert Schweitzer. Libby replied:

> I do not mean to say that there is no risk at all. What I should like to demonstrate to you is that the risk is extremely small compared with other risks which persons everywhere take as a normal part of their lives. At the same time I ask you to weigh this risk against what I believe to be the greater risk—to freedom—concerning people everywhere in the world—of not creating our defenses against the totalitarian forces at large in the world until such time as safeguarded disarmament may be achieved.[32]

Seldom has anyone in Libby's position as a government scientist put in such frank terms the continuity between technical, political,

[31] Quoted in *The New York Times* (June 29, 1956), p. 6.
[32] *BAS*, XIII, No. 6 (June 1957), p. 206.

and moral judgment which marks the role of the scientific adviser. But his candor did not dispose of the issues. It merely raised them in sharper form. Why should the government deliberately add to the risks of life? How could the AEC knowingly cause disfigurement (through genetic mutations resulting from bomb tests), cancer, and leukemia? Was the AEC entitled to make this decision for the American people and for others who would be hurt by the tests? Was it so certain that further development of hydrogen weapons was essential to our defense? Might it not be, on the contrary, that to proceed with testing weapons was to invite disaster by making it more difficult to get disarmament and by setting a precedent and a standard for states as yet without nuclear weapons? The scientists were generally agreed that the immediate danger from fallout was slight, but they disagreed over the possible extent of future damage and over the question of whether testing was, on the whole, desirable or undesirable.

The position of the scientists critical of the AEC policy emerged in the form of a political proposal put forward in the 1956 presidential campaign by Adlai E. Stevenson. Stevenson suggested a unilateral suspension of nuclear testing by the United States as a challenge and inducement to the Russians leading to an agreement to halt testing. Following the reasoning of his scientific advisers, Stevenson said that such an agreement ought not to be regarded as an end in itself but as a first step toward more directly important negotiated settlements. We must, he said, "get off the dead center of disagreement." In 1957, after Stevenson had been defeated, over 2,000 American scientists responded to Pauling's appeal for an international agreement to ban tests. Many others did not sign only because they disagreed with the reasons offered in the petition. In 1958 Senator Humphrey was to raise the issue in the political arena anew, this time from the floor of the Senate.

The initial position of the Eisenhower administration was that to stop testing without a workable scheme of inspection was to handcuff ourselves and to encourage the Russians to cheat. In addition, testing was held of significant military value since it would make possible the production of "cleaner" bombs producing less radioactive fallout, which would permit military invasion as a follow-up to an H-bomb attack and which would provide greater control of the effects of the bomb.

By the summer of 1958, however, administration policy had changed. President Eisenhower announced that the United States would suspend testing, and invited the Soviets to follow suit. A conference of experts from the Western countries and the U.S.S.R. met to consider methods of providing workable inspection. The meeting produced an encouraging amount of agreement on the possibility of detecting nuclear explosions by various methods. Not long after the meeting, however, the AEC tested a small underground device which it was claimed evaded detection by seismic indicators. This test and preliminary calculations of the effect of muffling the explosion, emanating principally from Teller and David Griggs at Livermore Laboratory, introduced doubts into the negotiations. In 1959, as negotiations dragged on, Teller and Albert Latter came up with what came to be known as the "Big Hole" theory. Their calculations demonstrated that it would be possible to conduct clandestine small-scale explosions in deep and large underground caverns excavated for that purpose. But analysis indicated that while such tests might well escape seismic detection, they would require a degree of effort, expense, and time that might not be expected to escape attention or to be worth undertaking. The advocates of the Geneva system had first answered that to detect small explosions it was necessary simply to increase the number of stations. Against the Big Hole theory they argued that tests would be detected by other means. But the argument often boiled down to a general difference of outlook. Speaking as one of those anxious to gain a negotiated settlement, Hans Bethe has noted that if as much effort were put into improving methods for detection as into the development of new bombs, agreement might be possible.[33] In a sense the argument was one between those willing to risk the danger that the Soviets might cheat on an agreement and those willing to risk the damage bomb testing may involve. Teller has suggested that those who advocate a test ban do so not because they are really concerned

[33] Hans Bethe, "The Case for Ending Nuclear Tests," *Atlantic Monthly* (August 1960), pp. 43-51.

over the effects of testing but because it is a convenient (however unwarranted) way of expressing their pacifistic viewpoint.[34] He has argued that only clean nuclear weapons of assorted size and form would make total war unlikely. From the other side it is argued that Teller has supported testing because his commitment is to military strength rather than to negotiation, but not because he really thinks the tests are harmless. As John M. Fowler has said of the controversy between Teller and Pauling,

> The two men were influenced in their interpretations by their sharply differing views on testing of nuclear bombs. Teller, believing strongly that leadership in nuclear weapons is the paramount requirement for the nation's safety, used the most optimistic estimates on the effects of fallout and emphasized the statistical insignificance of the possible danger. Pauling, convinced that continued testing of weapons will only push us more rapidly down the road toward nuclear annihilation, counted every life sacrificed as an inexcusable waste; he took the point of view that we should be cautious, should err on the side of pessimism, and laid stress on the number of victims rather than the small fraction of the population they represent.[35]

Missiles and Space: The Politics of Administration

Linked importantly to the testing controversy are developments in yet another new field of scientific weaponry, guided missiles. Advocates of testing have urged further experiments not only to secure "cleaner" bombs with less radioactive fallout, but also to develop smaller-size bombs of varying explosive force to be used as warheads for missiles. Before the Soviet Union resumed testing in September 1961, opponents of our entry into a test-ban agreement argued that the Russians would gain most from a continued moratorium on testing. Because of her lead in accurate long-range missiles capable of carrying heavy payloads, Russia did not need further testing to develop a thermonuclear missile capability. Nor would it be in her interest to give us the opportunity to continue developing low-yield weapons for use in missiles of

---

[34] Edward Teller and Albert E. Latter, *Our Nuclear Future* (New York: Criterion Books, 1958), Ch. XV, pp. 137-145.

[35] John M. Fowler, ed., *Fallout: A Study of Superbombs, Strontium 90 and Survival* (New York: Basic Books, 1960), p. 35.

smaller range and compact warheads with higher yields for long-range missiles. On the other hand, advocates of a test-ban, notably Bethe, have pointed out that if an agreement had been secured earlier, and if the Russians had observed it, we would now be in a far better position than they with respect to the development of the H-bomb, since the majority of Russian tests were made after 1955.[36] The resumption of testing, it was contended, would still benefit the Russians more than ourselves, because the range of Soviet atomic weapons was still inferior to ours before the moratorium on testing.

The present long-standing connection between thermonuclear weapons and guided missiles has involved still another facet of relations between government and scientists. The United States missile program dates back to the close of World War II when the Germans had pulled well ahead of the Allies with their V-1 and V-2 weapons. At the end of the War the Russians and the Americans descended on German missile installations looking for scientists and engineers and for facilities to turn to their own use. Our Operation Paperclip is said to have done better in terms of manpower; the Russians, better with respect to facilities. We rounded up a team of 130 men led by General Walter Dornberger and Werner von Braun. The first missiles produced both by the Russians and by the United States were copies of the German prototypes. Development in the early period did not proceed at a spectacular pace. Von Braun has said that had we given wartime priority to our postwar program the United States would have had the first ICBM by 1950 instead of by 1958. Von Braun was put in charge of an Army project at the Redstone Arsenal in Huntsville, Alabama, but he received little support. The Korean War caused a step-up in the work not only in the Army but in the Navy as well. In 1950 the Secretary of Defense appointed a special assistant as Director of Guided Missiles to coordinate the work. In 1951 the Air Force contracted with Convair to develop the Atlas missile.

The pace continued to be slow until late in 1953, when the Secretary of the Air Force appointed the Scientific Committee for Ballistic Missiles to appraise the course of development. The group was called together by Trevor Gardner, Special Assistant to the

[36] Hans Bethe, "The Case for Ending Nuclear Tests."

Secretary for Research and Development. It was headed by von Neumann, who was joined by Bradbury, L. A. Hyland of Bendix, Kistiakowsky, Lauritsen, Charles Lindbergh, Robert R. McMath of the University of Michigan, James W. McRae of Sandia, Jerome Weisner, and Allen Puckett of Hughes Aircraft. Technical support was provided by Drs. Ramo and Dean E. Wooldridge and the staff of the Ramo-Wooldridge Corporation. After studying the problem for several months, the Committee advised the Secretary that since the development of light-weight thermonuclear weapons of high yield could be regarded as assured, the long range ballistic missile would be an extremely important future weapon. The Committee was persuaded that the limited missile accuracy required for very powerful warheads could be attained in the near future. The Committee concluded that existing activity in the field was entirely inadequate and urged complete reorientation and vigorous expansion. After considerable delay, the Air Force accepted these recommendations and established what it called the Scientific-Industrial-Military Development Complex, composed of four groups: the Ballistic Missile Division, headed by General Bernard Schriever, to provide over-all project planning and management; Ramo-Wooldridge, as the coordinator of actual work and the provider of systems engineering; the Ballistic Missile Office, to handle procurement and contradicting; and the Strategic Air Command Training and Operation Group, in charge of providing operational capability for missile use.

Over a period of time, new members were added to the Committee and some of the original members retired. About two years after its formation, the Committee was transferred into the Office of the Secretary of Defense and was charged with advising him on the entire ballistic missile program, regardless of the service sponsoring the project. The Committee was dissolved early in 1961. It is striking that neither this Committee, nor any of the various new relations of scientists to the government resulting from the missile program, has involved scientists in the kind of policy differences that have appeared in connection with atomic energy. Each of the branches has "its own" scientists and they develop attachments which sometimes lead to competitive rivalries that have been helpful in some ways, harmful in others. The Air Force deputy chief of staff for space projects, General Irvine, has contended that interservice rivalry is "healthy" for the nation.[37] At the same time certain instances of costly duplication of effort and wasteful competition have come to light. In some cases when the government has competed against itself and against private contractors for key personnel, serious inefficiencies have resulted.

The Thor-Jupiter rivalry between the Air Force team of General Schriever and the Army team of General Medaris was the major instance of wasteful interservice rivalry uncovered. When the Army needed the technical assistance of an Air Force contractor, it was told by the Air Force that it would have to work with the contractor indirectly, through the Air Force. The Army charged that when it asked for information on the requirements of the Jupiter, so that work would be designed to suit them, the Air Force provided inadequate data. The Army retaliated by refusing to allow the Air Force to bring along its civilian contractors to an assessment of the Army program. When General Bernard Schriever visited the Army installations in April, 1957, he did so without Simon Ramo, who was in charge of the Air Force program. General Medaris explained: "I could not buy the idea of having our system evaluated by a man who invented a different one." Did Medaris expect that Schriever would withhold information from his technical director? "No," said Medaris to a Congressional inquiry, "it was not quite that unrealistic. But maybe it would make him know how I felt." [38]

The Army claimed Air Force roadblocks slowed its work and charged that the Air Force had refused to acknowledge a defect in parts provided to the Army. The two branches fought a research war over nose cones until the Air Force finally had to admit the Army had gotten the better of the political battle. The Navy meanwhile was assigned the mission of orbiting several satellites with its Vanguard project. When the rockets failed ignominiously the Army earnestly, but perhaps too solicitously, offered some of its Jupiter-C rockets. These were politely, but perhaps too proudly, refused.

After a series of such mixups and mishaps it was decreed that only

[37] *Hearings Before the Preparedness Investigating Subcommittee of the Senate Committee on Armed Services*, 85th Cong., 1st & 2nd sess. (Washington, D.C.: Government Printing Office, 1958), p. 967.

[38] *Organization and Management of Missile Programs, Hearings Before a Subcommittee of the House Committee on Government Operations*, 86th Cong., 1st sess. (Washington, D.C.: Government Printing Office, 1959), p. 281.

the Air Force would develop the land-based IRBM and ICBM; the Navy would develop the ship-based IRBM; and the Army would restrict itself to missiles of less than 200-mile range that could be integrated with its military mission and to other missiles designed for the defense of specific points. Later, the Army facilities and personnel were transferred to the newly created National Aeronautics and Space Administration which was to have charge of all space projects without military application.

The news that the Russians had orbited their first Sputnik had a sobering effect on the American program, even though there was at first some tendency on the part of high officials to belittle the Russian break into space as a clever stunt with no military significance. Nevertheless, all the missile programs were speeded up and reorganized shortly after the launching of the first Sputnik. The Department of Defense was also asked to proceed with the development of a solid-fuel rocket, an anti-missile missile, and early warning systems. Organizational experiments with a "missile czar" were abandoned, later to be followed by the creation of a Director of Research and Engineering and an Advanced Research Projects Agency. Meanwhile, President Eisenhower created the post of Special Assistant for Science and Technology and the President's Science Advisory Committee.

During 1958 it was decided to assign chief responsibility for space exploration to one agency, but there was no ready agreement over whether the agency should be civilian or military. The Air Force felt strongly that all space activities should be left to the DOD. General Schriever testified that 90 per cent of military missile developments would also apply to space satellites. Although Army and Navy spokesmen were not anxious to enhance an Air Force monopoly of space, they too preferred that the new agency be located within the DOD.

In opposition to military control of space exploration were administrators and scientists and, in a few cases, maverick military men like General Doolittle, General Gavin, and Admiral Rickover, who contended that only if the agency were civilian could interservice rivalry be avoided. They also contended that the services were relatively slow to accept new ideas and not in the habit of taking risks, whereas novelty and risk were essential in space research. Scientific associations also played an active role on the side of a civilian organization. The American Rocket Society submitted a report to the President recommending a civilian agency, as did the National Society of Professional Engineers, the International Geophysical Year Earth Satellite Panel, and others. The Federation of Atomic Scientists urged that the agency be set up on the model of the Atomic Energy Commission, lest space research be guided exclusively by military considerations and conducted under military control. The FAS and later Senator Humphrey advocated a Space Commission which, with NSF, AEC, and the Bureau of Standards, would be a component of a new Department of Science and Technology.

President Eisenhower leaned toward the idea of a civilian agency. He asked his Special Assistant, James R. Killian, Jr. to suggest a way of setting one up. Killian took counsel with Alan T. Waterman of the NSF and Detlev Bronk of the NAS. Killian also conferred with General Doolittle, the Chairman, and Hugh Dryden, the Director, of the National Advisory Committee for Aeronautics. The NACA, with a good record and good facilities, was thought to be in danger of expiring if it were excluded from space activities. Killian proposed that the NACA be the nucleus of a new space agency. The administration adopted the Plan, Congress approved it, and the National Aeronautics and Space Administration came into existence. The Department of Defense at first opposed the proposal and then, when it was all but certain to go into effect, concentrated its efforts upon urging Congress to amend the wording of the legislation so that NASA would be clearly subordinate to the DOD in military matters. After the bill was passed into law, other efforts were made to assure over-all coordination and review of space activities, military and civilian. A recent result is the increased importance of the National Space Council, of which Vice President Lyndon B. Johnson is Chairman.

Civil-military friction has also cropped up in other areas of government research administration. In 1959 Admiral Rickover told a Subcommittee of the House Committee on Government Operations that the ordinary vices of bureaucracy were often compounded by procedures in military research. Rickover endorsed intramural research over the contract system, but he pointed out that the advantages of such organization were usually lost because formal distinctions between military and civilian personnel were maintained without regard to efficiency. In his own bureau, Rickover said, "[W]e have civilians working for officers. We have officers working for civilians. We have had a lieutenant commander working for a Reserve lieutenant (jg). Whoever can do the job best gets the job and that is all there is to it." He agreed with Representative Holifield that different procedures are used in research organized by the Department of Defense. As he put it, with characteristic bluntness,

> Officers in the Pentagon get a tour of duty of 2 or 3 years, presumably to train them, but they are in charge. How can a man possibly take charge of complex technical matters, say a man who has been captain of a ship and has not had the requisite scientific and engineering training and experience?
>
> Why, it is an absurdity on the face of it, and this is where much of our difficulty starts, because as soon as he gets into one of these jobs with lots of authority and no responsibility, he remembers every idea he ever had from his high school days on, and he tries to put it into practice. And then, 2 or 3 years later, after he has finally learned something about his job, he goes to some other duty and a new untrained officer takes charge.[39]

If the military personnel were improperly used, the civilians were unable to make up for it.

> [M]any of the civilians who do stick around get beaten down in spirit . . . The present system encourages the good civilians to leave. So the situation in short is this: A constantly moving assembly line of officers is entering and taking charge. They are not necessarily more competent but they automatically take charge of the civilians. The civilians, by force of circumstances, have become dispirited, so we keep in the same rut all the time. Why, do you know that it is not possible for a civilian to get any of the leading positions in any of the technical bureaus of the Navy? I believe this applies to the other services, too. . . .
>
> So it boils down to this: We have, in effect, designated civilians as being inferior to officers, as second-class citizens, you might say. Do you really believe that the better people will remain in an organization on this basis?[40]

[39] *Ibid.,* pp. 606-607.
[40] *Ibid.,* p. 607.

Rickover also had a few words on the practice in the DOD of naming advisory panels or committees. After carefully distinguishing such committees from those of Congress, with which his own relations have always been most warm, he observed that the appointment of special *ad hoc* committees served three purposes: to provide support for a project desired by those making the appointment, or, after the project is in existence, to praise its operation; to permit an incoming director to find out what is going on without relying solely on what his own administrators tell him; and to "ax somebody or force a new project to be started." [41]

In addition, Rickover testified, the committee reports are often an expensive waste of time, since they are frequently couched in generalities and conceived without necessary technical understanding.

PSAC: A Policy Voice for Scientists

While questions of sheer administrative efficiency have loomed large in the relations of scientists to government space programs and research in general, they have not completely overshadowed political involvement. For this, thanks are again due to Sputnik. With the establishment of the Special Assistant for Science and Technology and the President's Science Advisory Committee, the role of scientists as regular policy advisers at the highest level has been accorded formal recognition, institutional legitimacy, and budgetary support. Through the Special Assistant, PSAC gives scientists unprecedented peacetime access to the President.

The first major policy controversy in which PSAC and the Special Assistant were put to the test concerned nuclear weapons testing.[42] In 1957, when the administration began to consider the possibilities of suspending testing in favor of seeking an agreement for control with the Russians, AEC Chairman Strauss had taken Lawrence and Teller to President Eisenhower in an effort to persuade him not to suspend testing so that scientists might continue to work on the development of "clean" bombs. Killian is said to have persuaded

[41] *Ibid.,* pp. 608-610.

[42] This account draws on Robert C. Toth, "The President's Science Advisory Committee," Paper Presented to the Science and Public Policy Seminar, Graduate School of Public Administration, Harvard University, May, 1961.

the President to listen to scientists on the other side of the controversy. Early in 1958, at the request of the President, Killian set up an interdepartmental panel to study the feasibility of monitoring a test ban. After two months of study the panel concluded that monitoring a ban was technically feasible. On the basis of this report, President Eisenhower and Secretary Dulles decided to propose an East-West conference of experts at Geneva to explore the technical possibilities, preparatory to an agreement to establish a control system. The Geneva conferees came to an agreement, but shortly thereafter studies undertaken at Livermore Laboratory and by the RAND Corporation indicated that the technical basis of the "Geneva system" was inadequate. The United States was compelled to withdraw its agreement to the Geneva system under fire of Soviet propaganda which insisted that our intentions had been insincere from the start. The PSAC panel was criticized for having submitted a report based on inadequate research in order to provide support for a particular policy. But this weakness was clearly pointed out in its report. PSAC can be credited with promoting an exploration of the technical problems and testing the Soviet willingness to negotiate the issue, which may have long term benefits.

A PSAC panel also played an important role with respect to another military-scientific issue, the nuclear-powered airplane. In 1958 the AEC and Air Force met post-Sputnik anxiety with the proposal for a crash program on this project, which had been in process since the end of the War and had cost nearly a billion dollars by then. A PSAC panel concluded that while much progress had been made on subsidiary problems, the key issue—the design of a nuclear reactor efficient enough to serve as the prime source of power for the aircraft's engines—was far from solved. The only reactor at all in sight would require such heavy shielding that the aircraft might not even rise from the ground and would be in the best case very inferior to jet-powered aircraft, except possibly for range. The panel concluded that what was sorely needed was not an engineering crash project but some sound research to discover ways in which efficient high temperature reactors could be constructed. High officials in the DOD agreed with these conclusions but were reluctant to take them to Congress without the support of the panel's report, which was a privileged document of the White House. The panel was therefore reconstituted within the DOD so that its findings might be presented to Congress. Congress was not convinced and continued to appropriate huge sums for the project. The Defense Department and the administration felt compelled to divert these to other uses. The Kennedy administration has pressed further to downgrade the project.

When Kistiakowsky succeeded Killian as Special Assistant, PSAC, in the course of advising the President on various military "hardware" proposals, took a stand against an expansion of the B-70 supersonic bomber project advocated by the Air Force. The main arguments against this multi-billion dollar program are supposed to be that by the time the B-70 becomes operational, ballistic missiles would provide a far less costly, speedier, and less vulnerable means for the delivery of nuclear explosives. Furthermore, by the time the B-70 could be produced, even on a crash basis, the Soviets would have perfected their air defenses to a point where even a supersonic bomber would be a "sitting duck." Finally, the B-70 could not be protected against a nuclear blast, as an ICBM could be if it were put underground. A B-70 force, therefore, could not be regarded as a secure deterrent. Whether because of these arguments or of others, the B-70 program was given somewhat lower priority.

On these important occasions PSAC has provided scientists with a high-level official channel for their points of view on military and strategic matters. Equally noteworthy is the fact that PSAC also gives scientists an unprecedented opportunity to assess and to contribute to government policy on science itself. The period during which the nation's enormous scientific establishment was developed was also one during which the political activity of the scientists was concentrated largely on the military applications of their discipline. Meanwhile, with the exception of the debates on the AEC and the NSF, the scientists were largely silent on many of the substantive policies that most closely affected their profession.

The change which PSAC has wrought in this regard is perhaps best exemplified by some of the more recent reports to emanate from the White House. The studies of three different PSAC panels deserve particular mention: *Strengthening American Science* (1958),

Education for the Age of Science (1959), and *Scientific Progress, the Universities and the Federal Government* (1960). The first of these is perhaps the best known, because it prompted the creation of the Federal Council for Science and Technology. It also dealt with key problems of research planning, working conditions in government laboratories, the administrative problems of contracting institutions, especially universities, and the question of capital facilities for scientific research. In *Education for the Age of Science,* PSAC examined various aspects of the educational system, including course curricula and teacher training. *Scientific Progress, the Universities and the Federal Government* offers some reasoned opinions concerning federal-university relations.

In all these instances PSAC has provided scientists with a long-needed policy voice. The most important policy decisions will of course continue to be made by the highest elected and administrative officials, but the presence of science in the White House signifies a great improvement in the relations between scientists and government, and one that represents for the scientists an opportunity neither to dictate nor to abdicate, but to help shape science policy as responsible professionals.

CONCLUSION

CONCLUSION:

POLICY AND POLITICS

How shall we account for and evaluate the developments de-scribed in this study? C. P. Snow, in his typically provocative man-ner, has proposed a distinction between the older industrial revo-lution and the modern "scientific revolution." There are limitations to this characterization, as there are to all attempts to classify and label segments of history, but it is a useful one to bear in mind in reflecting upon the American experience with science and tech-nology in recent decades.

This much is surely plain:

As the state of technology becomes more complex, economically advanced nations must spend a sizeable part of their national in-come on behalf of immediate and long-range innovation. The result is that both security and welfare depend less upon sheer productive capacity and natural resources and more upon scientific research and development. Increasingly, science plays a crucial role in the economy, in military preparedness, and even in the quest for pres-tige that symbolizes the competition among the nations. In the United States, these new demands have led the government to ex-pand its traditional concern for national development and welfare to include large-scale sponsorship of scientific research carried out by industry, the universities, and government agencies. In the proc-ess, government has naturally come to require the advice and judg-ment of scientists over a wide range of important policy questions. To this extent at least, America may be said to be be experiencing the scientific revolution—as a continuation or concomitant of the industrial revolution.

However we designate these changes, we should not lose sight of them. In themselves and in the implications they bear for the direction of American government and politics, they are surely of serious historical significance. This is especially the case with respect to the two parallel lines of development that we have stressed in this study. As we have seen, government sponsorship of research has led to an unprecedented breach of the traditional wall between public and private institutions and to a similar breach of the line that is usually drawn between the policy-maker and the technical adviser. In the sponsorship of research, public and private institutions are linked in a partnership that seems to be permanent; in political decisions affecting science, technical advice and policy-making go hand in hand. These two developments lie at the heart of what may be called the American experience of the scientific revolution.

The traditional principles that are being altered by these developments are of course well known, even to the point of considerable exaggeration. Politicians and publicists continue to exploit widespread fears either that government is crushing private initiative or that private interest dictates public policy. If there is any political cliché more popular than these it is the belief that in some dark way experts are "taking over" from both the government and private interests. The value of the experiences examined in this study lies not so much in the novelty of the problems they raise as in the opportunity they provide for a concrete and realistic examination of these issues so often obscured or colored by dogmatic interpretation.

Admittedly we have ourselves emphasized the constructive possibilities inherent in both lines of development at the risk of minimizing the dangers. We have described the relations among government, industry, and the universities as a partnership rather than as a doubtful confusion of role. We have described the involvement of the scientists in the shaping of defense policy as an example of professional responsibility and not as usurpation of authority by experts or as a suborning of their noble pursuit to the base ends of war. We have done so in order to call attention to the efforts that have been made to meet the need for effective scientific research and scientific advice in ways congenial to the spirit of the American political tradition.

Surely it is striking that, both in the area of policy and in the area of politics, older, more dogmatic lines have been broken by new arrangements bringing greater cooperation without radical social reorganization. An inflexible boundary between public and private would have made impossible the revolution in government science. An unbending separation of technical and policy advice would have done incalculable harm to military planning, as rapidly became obvious in the one major instance where such a separation was tried. If science and the nation have become interdependent but not indistinguishable it is because implicitly and explicitly those who have shaped the relationship have recognized that cooperation is essential if free institutions and individual freedom are to continue to function successfully. They have therefore sought to answer a national need but at the same time to promote institutional pluralism and personal responsibility.

It would be folly, of course, to shut our eyes blindly to the difficulties and dangers of such readjustments simply because they strike a hopeful balance between traditional values and contemporary needs. In a partnership in which private and public ends coexist, or in which different public ends must compete, it is bound to be difficult to achieve universal satisfaction. If technical advisers become more authoritative than their knowledge warrants, or if only one set of advisers gains the confidence of the political leadership, the delicate balance can be rudely upset. So that the problematic character of these new departures will become sufficiently evident to help the reader make his own evaluation, it will be useful here to review some of the major issues raised in both phases of this study.

Public and Private: The Diplomacy of Partnership

The present establishment for scientific research and development entails federal expenditure at a rate approaching $10 billion per year, and additional billions are being spent to subsidize the training of potential scientists and engineers. As a government spending program, science is now second only to military hardware procurement and Armed Forces personnel. It has become a fiscal giant that surpasses even agricultural price supports.

The bulk of federal science expenditure is being devoted to the support of military R & D performed by business firms. In the pursuit of national security through research and development, government and industry have developed a partnership without precedent. In a very real sense, this partnership has the net effect of making government more like business and business more like government.

Military R & D juxtaposes the traditional roles of government and industry. Through the cost-reimbursement contract, government assumes the classic business role of the entrepreneur, the financial risk-taker. On the other hand, private business, because of its research and managerial capacities, assumes a substantial role in shaping military and strategic policies. Moreover, since government does not have the capacity to supervise closely every phase of weapons development, business acquires a joint administrative responsibility for the expenditure of public money. In subcontracting, this responsibility includes participation in such important public policies as fostering small business and giving aid to economically depressed areas. At several junctures, business assumes public functions, while government performs the task of innovator.

The altered roles of government and business are largely the result of technological requirements. The principles of the market economy that are embodied in fixed price contracting cannot be applied to the procurement of research. In R & D, uncertainty is so great and the financial stakes so high that business cannot afford the risks and government cannot supply all of the needed scientific and managerial skills.

When the automatic regulation of the open market can no longer be applied to government-business relations, the only remaining checks on abuse are administrative in nature. Administration is seldom easy and never automatic, but the development of its tools will determine the satisfactory operation of the partnership between government and business.

Although this partnership has been made to work with fair efficiency, possible abuses will remain a challenge to the administra-

tive skills and the mutual good will of each of the partners. Neither
side can afford to take undue advantage of the other. The government, through irrational and thoughtless budgetary cuts, can easily
wreck carefully chosen industrial research teams. Excessive red tape
and petty administrative annoyances can lengthen the time needed
to bring projects to completion.

Because industry is not so closely subject to the public con-
stituency as government, private abuses of public responsibility are
always a great potential danger. Business firms are under constant
temptation to pad the cost estimates on which their fees are based.
They can use special knowledge acquired in publicly supported
work to violate the canons of free competition. They can try to
pressure the government into embarking on wasteful programs that
will result only in public loss and private gain. In brief, the survival and the potential achievements of a government-business partnership depend on a delicate balance of trust and cooperation.

The challenge posed by this alliance between public and private institutions is no less in the relationship between government
and universities than in that between government and business.
Understandably, however, the terms of the government-university
partnership are different. The function of the universities has
always been to advance knowledge and educate men. As such,
institutions of higher education have had as their goal not private gain but the advancement of learning. Until recently, they
pursued their goal either as independent institutions or under the
sponsorship of state governments.

Today, the relative independence of universities from the federal government has been rudely shattered. The government has embarked on a deliberate policy of heavy subsidy to university research,
both in pure science and in applied fields related to defense and
health. Contracts and grants by the thousands have invaded the
campus. University administrators and scientists find themselves
immersed in the legalistic world of "Circular A-21," matching grants,
and secrecy regulations.

The government has decided that research is not the only public need to be fulfilled by universities; many more scientists and
engineers must be educated to meet the requirements of a technologically advanced society. Accordingly, fellowships, loans, and facili-

ties grants are beginning to have a profound effect on the teaching, as well as the research, side of the university equation. Furthermore, new programs of federal aid to primary and secondary schools will only have the net effect of increasing popular demand for university education. On all sides, universities now find themselves firmly constituted as important components of public policy.

The difficulties of a close partnership between government and universities are both numerous and dangerous. While universities are entirely preoccupied with education, the federal government pursues policies in many areas, of which education is but one. It is in the very nature of a university to be jealous of its independence and individuality. But since the government must reconcile many different demands, some of which may often be in conflict with others, the delicacy of government-university relations is bound to be extreme. The principal danger is that the timeless values of higher education will be sacrificed for too immediate needs. Government can stifle intellectual inquiry through overly stringent administrative and security regulations. In legislating for spending programs without due regard to over-all educational needs, government can create financial problems that in the long run will seriously threaten university welfare.

On their side, universities run the risk of becoming passive and complacent. As important components of public policy, they now have a duty and a responsibility constantly to remind public officials of the special nature of higher education. In this they fail at their peril, for federal policies will not be tailored to truly educational needs unless universities act as vigilant partners.

The partnership of public and private, of government, business, and education, will not work to optimal capacity on its own. It can serve the nation with full efficiency only if each of the partners exercises the restraint, the diplomacy, and the cooperation that are the basis of sound alliances. In our examination of the workings of the partnership, we have occasionally noted where certain general improvements might be made. Are these improvements reasonably attainable? Only time will tell, but one condition stands out above all others. It is the very thread that links the partnership, namely, science itself.

Greater concern for the special nature of science can polish many of the rough edges of the public-private partnership. It can help free scientists of excessive red tape in their work. It can lead the government to formulate less arbitrary budgetary policies in military R & D. An effort to distinguish more carefully between research and production can reduce military lead times and stimulate greater competition among business firms.

In questions affecting universities, greater concern for science becomes greater concern for higher education. It can promote more basic research and more liberal administrative and financial policies. It underlines the necessity for comprehensive analysis of the total impact of manpower programs on educational institutions, on research and teaching.

It is only reasonable that science should hold the key to the success of a public-private partnership that has been created to satisfy technological needs. The partnership must survive if the nation is to achieve security and welfare, but it will remain a constant organizational challenge to responsible policy-makers.

Professional Responsibility: The Experience of the Scientists

If the institutional partnership is likely to be permanent, for better or worse, the continuing political role of the scientists is probably no less certain, although it may never again be as intense as it was in the case of the atomic scientists just after the War.

It is plausible to suppose that the atomic scientists have been so active in such numbers because their particular experience has been unique. It was precisely in the period of transition in which science was transformed into an indispensable source of political power that the atomic scientists first came into contact with government. They were, in other words, the scientists who experienced the shock of transition. Is it possible that the variety of their commitments was linked to the uniqueness of their experience? Will the shock wear off and give way to the kind of political conformity that seems to characterize the space scientists? Were the atomic scientists a kind of avant-garde for nonmilitary expertise in strategy-making? Now that the hitherto exclusive preserve of soldiers and statesmen has been successfully breached, will the scientists tend to defer to the judgment of other professionals—such as the specialists in the application of game theory to international relations, or even to specialists of more traditional character—who have since entered these areas? The case of Herman Kahn, to take a leading example, is instructive. Kahn was trained as a physicist, but it is as a specialist in military strategy and applied game theory, not as a physicist, that he contributes to policy-making.

These questions are easier raised than resolved, partly because the evidence is limited and partly because the answers may well depend on the effect of unforeseeable events. In so far as experience is any guide, it will help to re-examine what has happened so far, on the side of the atomic scientists and on the side of the government, for what it indicates in general about the role of scientists in politics.

Having made their first approach to government in an effort simply to confer an instrument of power, the atomic scientists then moved to influence the use of atomic energy by efforts at public education and legislative lobbying. When these efforts proved inadequate they turned to the more direct avenue of participation in the formation and implementation of strategic policy. In this phase they experienced sharp splits within their ranks. It became clear that scientists divided into distinct groups. At one end of the spectrum were those advocating pacifism and withdrawal, at the other those inclined to work for success in the arms race. In the middle were one group working on behalf of limited war, defense, and negotiation as a step toward ultimate pacification, and another committed to a policy of offensive strength or deterrence as the best means of preventing a large-scale war. Depending on their inclinations in these directions, scientists have also divided in their attitude toward the dangers of fallout and radioactivity and toward the prospects for agreements to control testing. (This is not to suggest that scientists inevitably take sides according to their political predispositions but only that their judgment is likely to be influenced by them, especially when the evidence on either side is incomplete and needs to be weighed for significance.)

As the Cold War deepened, the advocates of the policy of strength rose in power while those critical of this policy fell from official grace. They fell so far that their leading representative was subjected to public disgrace in a security inquiry prompted by his opposition to official policy. Their cause was revived as Congress developed an interest in criticism of the executive and a concern for the dangers of weapons testing. The executive followed the lead of Congress toward this more receptive attitude as it had earlier followed the lead of Congress in the direction of suspicion and distrust. It was a State Department still under Dulles which sent American scientists to Geneva to negotiate a test ban. And it was in the same administration that had earlier developed the criterion of "security risk" that PSAC and the Office of Special Assistant to the President for Science and Technology were set up, providing direct access to the executive for scientists who found the way blocked or uncongenial in other agencies. In 1960 both parties for the first time appointed committees on science and technology to advise framers of the party platforms.

If only because these experiences have brought about a certain habit of mutual recognition, accommodation, and confidence on the part of both scientists and government, it would seem likely that for the foreseeable future scientists in all the disciplines will continue to play an important role in politics. Indeed, it would appear from present tendencies that this role will be regularly pursued on all levels—in public debate, legislative activity and inquiry, and executive policy-making and implementation. It may be that the exploration of space and the further development of space weapons will for a time make space scientists more prominent than some of those who have in the past represented the concerns of scientists. It is also possible that, as population and natural resource pressures grow, and as scientific research assumes greater economic and ecological importance, a broader group of scientists may develop political concerns of a still different kind. But it seems likely that, whoever the representatives are, they will feel impelled to fill the roles already established by others.

Whatever the distant future may hold, it is clear from what has already been experienced that scientists, like the members of many professions, are called upon in modern times to play a larger role in politics than ever before. The dangers that result in considerable measure from the growing complexity of science and technology can only be met with the help of those capable of understanding and anticipating the problems. No great nation can afford any longer to dispense with the advice and creative foresight of its leading scientists and engineers. The cost and complexity of weapons systems and the speed with which they become obsolete make it imperative that scientists play important advisory roles. The destructive dimensions of many modern weapons—physical, chemical, biological, and radiological—are so unprecedented and so uncertain that no nation can consider using or even testing them without the reassurance of specialists in various of the disciplines and subdisciplines of the natural sciences. The prospects for agreements to control armament or to disarm depend as much upon science as upon political utility. Such agreements can now be drawn only on terms suggested by scientists, who alone are able to devise systems of inspection and probe for techniques of evasion. To the extent that international conflict is exacerbated by suspicion and misunderstanding, international meetings such as the Pugwash Conferences in recent years can contribute significantly to the relief of extraneous tensions.

The new political role of the scientists is not without dangers. In the past political leaders have sometimes made the mistake of consulting only those scientists who provided technical support to their policy preferences. Even if future leaders should be wiser, they will still face the very hard task of deciding among competing technical judgments in matters where they are all but wholly incompetent. It is sometimes suggested that the way out of this difficulty is to make sure that political leaders receive a scientific education. No doubt there is some degree of merit to this proposal, but a moment's reflection will make it obvious to anyone that this solution will not seriously affect the problem. No education in general science could possibly enable a politician to match his judgment against professional scientific specialists. The burden must fall upon the scientists, as upon other professionals, to act always with a sense of special responsibility. Where bureaucratic inertia on the one hand, and popular ignorance, incompetence, and apathy on the other, threaten to impose a policy of drift and intermittent panic, the exercise of professional responsibility is vital. The scientists who have striven in the past two decades to provide both political leaders and the general public with an education to the need for choice have done a great national service. They will continue to do so as long as there is enough recognition, within the government and outside, that scientists of all shades of opinion are valuable counsellors, and as long as there is a realization on the part of the scientists that politics may be a demanding art even if it is not an exact science.

The Need for Public Understanding

The two developments that we have been describing as incidents of the scientific revolution in the United States are both proceeding without any particularly active public awareness. Some might argue that where the changes in traditional practice are as delicate as these, it is best that this should be so. But there are times in our system of government when, quite apart from the ideals of democracy, public understanding is extremely important. This is one of those times. Without better public understanding, it will not be easy to achieve a healthy balance among government, business, and universities. Inevitably, short-run goals will be the ones to arouse support to the neglect of long-run institutional and scientific needs. Without public understanding of the value and limitations of their advisory function, scientists who are active in politics may find themselves deified one day and denounced the next. Without public understanding of the new ways of partnership in which science and the nation have been brought together, old ideological dogmas may hinder vital progress. In the last analysis, a democratic nation can cope with the scientific revolution wisely only if thoughtful citizens know what it truly entails.